LIVING THINGS
How To Know Them

An illustrated key to the phyla, classes and
more important orders of Plants and Animals
with suggestions for studying them.

Revised Edition

H. E. JAQUES

Professor Emeritus of Biology
Iowa Wesleyan College

WM. C. BROWN   COMPANY   PUBLISHERS
135 SOUTH LOCUST STREET   •   DUBUQUE, IOWA 52003

THE PICTURED-KEY NATURE SERIES

"How to Know the Insects," Jaques, 1947

"Living Things—How to Know Them," Jaques, 1946

"How to Know the Trees," Jaques, 1946

"Plant Families—How to Know Them," Jaques, 1948

"How to Know the Economic Plants," Jaques, 1948, 1958

"How to Know the Spring Flowers," Cuthbert, 1943, 1949

"How to Know the Mosses and Liverworts," Conard, 1944, 1956

"How to Know the Land Birds," Jaques, 1947

"How to Know the Fall Flowers," Cuthbert, 1948

"How to Know the Immature Insects," Chu, 1949

"How to Know the Protozoa," Jahn, 1949

"How to Know the Mammals," Booth, 1949

"How to Know the Beetles," Jaques, 1951

"How to Know the Spiders," Kaston, 1952

"How to Know the Grasses," Pohl, 1953

"How to Know the Fresh-Water Algae," Prescott, 1954

"How to Know the Western Trees," Baerg, 1955

"How to Know the Seaweeds," Dawson, 1956

"How to Know the Freshwater Fishes," Eddy, 1957

"How to Know the Weeds," Jaques, 1959

"How to Know the Water Birds," Jaques-Ollivier, 1960

"How to Know the Butterflies," Ehrlich, 1961

"How to Know the Eastern Land Snails," Burch, 1962

"How to Know the Grasshoppers," Helfer, 1963

"How to Know the Cacti," Dawson, 1963

Other Subjects in Preparation

INTRODUCTION

MAN is the queerest of all living things; nevertheless the other 1,165,999 are each well worth knowing. No finer avocational program, no more necessary background for culture can be found than through intimate acquaintance with the myriad forms of life, scattered world wide.

It would require long rows of book shelves to hold the volumes telling about plants and animals. Many other highly interesting and valuable facts remain to be discovered. The best way after all to know these intriguing creatures is to live with them.

The aim of this book is to make relatively easy for any one who is willing to devote a little time to it, to answer the ever occuring question about plants and animals, — "What is it?" Of course, it is impossible to describe the more than one million known living things in one book or set of books.

Plants and animals fall into a few great groups which may be easily recognized. The scheme is the same the world over and a knowledge of these groups and sub-groups helps to understand any species from any region. Most of the important orders are included in the keys. For each order one or more fairly common representatives are pictured, and the relative size indicated. If this book helps to increase the love of Nature's creatures, through a better knowledge of them, the author will feel well repaid.

Many good friends helped with the keys and with other valuable suggestions. We cannot begin to name all who deserve credit. Miss Elizabeth Blagg and Professor Edwin L. Miller (ably aided by his charming wife) assisted in large ways with drawings and key suggestions. The unfailing patience and skill of Arlene Kneis and Martha W. Jaques, who had the major responsibility for the drawings, made the task easier. We are highly grateful to all these named and unnamed assistants.

The book, first published in 1939 has had corrections and minor changes made in its reprintings. Now it has been thoroughly revised and brought up to date. In our post-war globe trotting, something like this will be needed more than ever before.

Mt. Pleasant, Iowa,
March, 1946.

CONTENTS

LIVING THINGS — SOME COMPARISONS

 HAT is life?" Men through all the ages have puzzled over that question and the riddle is yet unsolved. A stone is interesting but it always remains the same. Any activity or change for it must come from the outside.

Livings things are born, grow, move; each plays its part, forms others of its kind; then presently dies. This life span for some species is completed in less than a day; others require many years in which to do their work; a few live to bind milleniums together. When Abraham was saying good-bye to the home folks, preparatory to starting westward to found a new nation, some trees still living today were sturdy saplings well on their long and notable life.

Living things have definite size; each species varies only within rather restricted limits, though the different species range from microscopic forms to great bulky creatures. Some tiny plants (bacteria, etc.) and animals (protozoa) are so small as to require the most powerful microscopes to reveal them. The Sulphur-bottom whale is the largest animal. It reaches a length of almost one hundred feet and may weigh close to 150 tons. The bulkiest living plant is the Big Tree or Giant Sequoia which attains a height of 325 feet and a trunk diameter of more than 35 feet. Some of these trees, growing in California, are thought to be at least 3000 years old. Some climbing vines of the tropics, as well as some of the brown algae growing in the ocean, attain a length of several hundred feet. Non-living bodies have no size limits; a variety of granite may be represented by a tiny grain of sand or a whole mountain; water may exist as a small drop or as a great ocean.

Each species of animal or plant life has its own definite form. Non-living things may assume any shape.

Non-living things do not reproduce themselves. The most urgent purpose of plants and animals is to reproduce others of their own kind. The constancy and faithfulness with which this is done perpetuates a species through millions of generations without marked change.

From very early times man has doubtless been giving names to the plants and animals which most pointedly touched his life. Aristotle, who died 322 B. C., was apparently the first to carefully study living things and attempt to classify them.

When Linnaeus in 1735 published the first edition of his "Systema Naturae" and introduced the system of binomial nomenclature, a new interest was aroused in plant and animal life and many scientists volunteered in the task of discovering, describing and naming the world's living things. Some of them have shown poor judgment; a few have been self seekers. The work still goes on. On the whole it is being done well.

SCIENTIFIC NAMES

This array of living things, known to science, now totals well over one million species. If we are to understand plants and animals in their relation to each other, some scheme of arrangement or classification is necessary. Accordingly the two kingdoms have each been divided into Phyla and these major groups divided in turn into Classes, Orders, Families, Genera and Species.

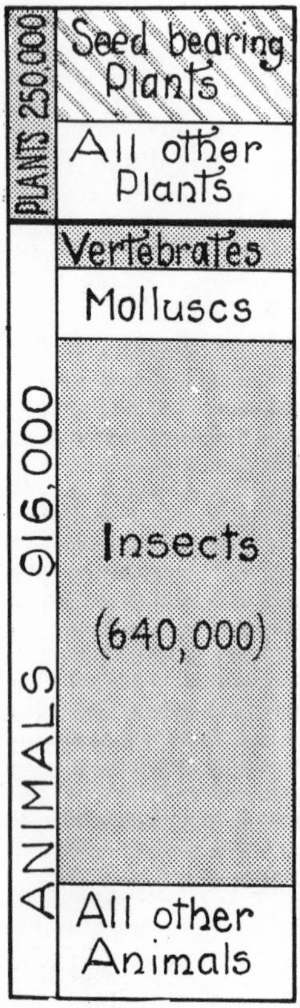

Figure 1
Relative Proportions
of the 1,166,000
Living Things

If we were to build a great museum of all these known plants and animals we could establish two large parks, one for the Plant Kingdom, the other for the Animal Kingdom. In the one we would erect 15 buildings for the 15 phyla of Plants. In the other park 16 buildings would be needed for each to shelter one phylum of Animals. Since there is much diversity in the number of species in a phylum the buildings would vary greatly in size. Each wing of a building would be devoted to one Class. The wings would be divided into rooms, each to house one Order; each room would contain shelves, some many, others few, each shelf to hold a Family. On the shelves would be boxes each for a Genus and within each box, bottles to contain the Species. Then, if we were placing some living thing in this museum or were wishing to examine some animal or plant already there, we would need to know to which park, which building, which room, which shelf, to go. Finally on this shelf we would need to find the right box and in it locate the right bottle. *Classification* is like that. If we follow the logical steps in an orderly way it is not particularly difficult and for many is highly fascinating. Some careful work in this opens up an altogether new view of the world about us.

Every species of plant and animal has a two-worded "scientific" name. The first is the Genus and begins with a capital letter; the second word is the Species. Zoologists begin all species names with small letters. Many botanists wish to follow the same rule for their plant names, while other botanists prefer to capitalize some species names. These scientific names are the same in all parts of the world. For that, as well as other reasons, they are much more accurate than common names.

Students sometimes regard the learning of scientific names as a great hardship. In fact while often unusual, they are no harder than telephone, automobile, velocipede and dozens of other household words of our three-year-olds.

2

MORE THAN 100 SUGGESTIONS
FOR NATURE STUDY PROJECTS

EVERY wide-awake teacher knows the intimate relation of work projects to the learning process. The Biological field offers exceptional opportunities for activities of this kind. In the main the best projects are those that involve local materials and conditions and which arise out of the students own experiences and desire to know. The suggestions which follow are for the most part simple. They have all been used many times and are workable but even then may well be modified to suit the temperament of the users. Just as the fond father may be counted upon to wear out his small son's Christmas toys, the teacher is often tempted to assume too much of the responsibility in project work. After all it is the students and not the teacher who are taking the course and the work, the responsibility and the thrill of achievement should be largely theirs.

Living animals may very profitably be brought to the school room for study. Every effort, however, should be made to maintain comfortable living conditions for these captive guests and to return them to their native habitat out of doors as early as possible. Dr. Hornaday has put it aptly "Being a pet is at best a hazardous occupation". Any nature study project that results in cruelty or needless destruction of plant or animal life in a measure defeats its own aims, and is not justified.

1. Make a collection of *WEED SEEDS* or seeds of cultivated plants. After they are cleaned and dried they may be kept in glass vials of uniform size, or round holes may be cut from heavy cardboard and the seeds mounted in these between two pieces of glass. Be sure to record the date they were collected.

2. *GERMINATE* weed or other seeds and study the early stages of the plants.

3. If *OLD SEEDS* of known age are available plant them or germinate between blotters to find which plant seeds live the longest and what percentage lose their viability each year.

4. Make *KEYS* to identify the seeds in your collection. Have someone else try the keys to see if they will work.

5. Compute the number of seeds produced by several plants of the same species to determine the *PROLIFICACY* of these plants.

6. Make *HERBARIUMS* of native or cultivated plants. The loose leaf scrap books to be found in the 10c stores are excellent in

Figure 2

size and appearance and cost but little. Fig. 2.*

7. Carefully *PRESSED PLANTS* may be mounted on 4x6 or larger cards and covered with a cellophane for wall display or use in class.

8. *INK LEAVES* on a rubber stamp pad and make a collection of leaf prints. Fig. 3.

9. *LEAF PRINTS* may be made directly on blue print or other photographic paper. Put the leaf over the face of the paper, clamp into a printing frame, expose to the light and develop.

Figure 3

10. Put neat *MARKERS* showing their common and scientific names on the shrubs and trees on your campus, school 'grounds, or nearby park. Heavy manilla shipping tags lettered with India ink, then dipped in melted paraffin, are good for a few years. There are many forms or more permanent labels.

11. Make a collection of *FERNS*, either living or pressed.

12. *FERN SPORES* may be readily germinated if covered with glass to retain the humity. A still better plan is to plant the spores on nutritive agar in wide mouthed bottles. Keep tightly corked.

13. Find how many species of animals are *ASSOCIATED* in some way with some one species of plant. Divide them into two groups, harmful or beneficial to the plant.

14. Establish a *BIRD FEEDING* station.

15. If *FISH* are available, study their age by the markings on the scales.

16. It is well worth anyones time to find from an indoor collection that *SNAKES* are not "slimy" and that most of them are not at all dangerous.

17. Get and keep a *PUFF ADDER* for a department pet. It may be safely handed to anyone as it will not bite.

18. *SNAKES* may be put in preservative in large glass tubes and sealed in by melting and closing the end of the tube.

19. The results of some common *VITAMINE DEFICIENCIES* may be pointedly illustrated with living mice, rats or sparrows.

20. Some demonstration cages of *MUTANT MICE* teach some facts about heredity more forcefully than lecturing or preaching.

---

*See "How to Make a Herbarium" in **How to Know the Spring Flowers,** Cuthbert.

NATURE STUDY PROJECTS

21. *SPATTER WORK* may be used to make a collection of leaf outlines. Fig. 4.

22. Students learn much by making wax or plaster *MODELS* of some plants or animals they study. Such models become permanently useful for illustrative purposes.

23. Except for large museums the collecting of bird eggs or bird skins does not seem justified. *BIRD NESTS*, after they have been abandoned, may be profitably collected and studied.

Figure 4

24. *CHARTS OF BIRDS* observed, with the dates, are valuable especially when kept over a period of years.

25. Much valuable information about birds is being found by *BIRD BANDING*. This fascinating activity could well be pursued by many more nature lovers.

26. Maintain a *BULLETIN BOARD* with good biological photos, pictures and clippings. Encourage your students to contribute materials for it.

27. Many free government and state *BULLETINS* are highly useful. Do not ask for more than you can profitably use.

28. Artificial *ANT NESTS* are easily maintained indoors and attract much attention.

29. Encourage students to bring *UNUSUAL PLANTS* or *ANIMALS* to school for class display and identification.

30. Make a collection of *LIVING SNAILS*. Remember that some are aquatic while others will not stay in water.

31. Cigar boxes may be lined with colored paper and *SNAIL SHELLS* or other mollusk shells glued to the bottom to make an attractive and useful collection.

32. Have the students look for *FROG, TOAD* or *SALAMANDER EGGS* in the spring. Keep small quantities of these eggs in shallow pans of fresh water and observe their development.

33. There is much beauty in the roadside plants and weeds after they have been killed by the frost. Have a *WINTER BOUQUET* contest and give simple prizes for the most beautiful arrangement of these dead plants in their natural colors.

34. Careful search will locate *HYDRA, PLANARIA* or *FRESH WATER SPONGES* in many regions where they are not known to live.

35. A *GALLON GLASS JUG* makes a fine receptacle for demonstrating the cooperation of aquatic plants and animals through their respiration and photosynthesis. Fill the jug to a depth of one inch with mud from the bottom of a pond, creek or other water course,

Figure 5

then put in pond water to half fill the jug. Add two or three good aquatic plants from a fish aquarium such as Elodea, Vallisnaria or Cabomba. Then put in a small Gold Fish. Drive the cork tightly into the bottle, wire it down and cover with wax. (That pleases the public even though it was air tight before.) Put a label on the jug giving the date and stating the purpose of your experiment. Put the jug in a well lighted place with moderate temperature and see how long the fish lives. (We had one like this that lasted 8 months and 13 days.) Fig. 5.

36. Require your students to make a carefully pinned, neatly labeled INSECT COLLECTION.*

37. By use of KEYS let each determine the orders and families of insects in his collection.

38. Appoint one or more of the best interested students as "Curator" and build a SCHOOL COLLECTION OF INSECTS.

39. Give SPECIAL MENTION of some sort to students who find specimens of species not already in the school collection.

40. Students with artistic ability will be interested in PAINTING some of the more colorful insects.

41. Collaborate with your Art teacher in furnishing insect specimens from which her classes may work out BORDER DESIGNS and COLOR PATTERNS. Insects cannot be beaten for this.

42. Make a collection of DRY FRUITS and determine how each is disseminated.

43. A TERRARIUM with desert plants and animals may be readily set up and maintained in a glass aquarium and is always profitable.

44. A project of TRAPPING the small rodents of a region may be followed up by making a careful COLLECTION OF SKINS for reference.

45. Take several field trips in the Fall to determine which PLANTS ARE KILLED by light frosts and which are killed only by hard freezing.

46. Encourage the making of neat, carefully named COLLECTIONS. Many boys and girls find their first real interest in school in this way.

47. Announce a TURTLE RACE, INSECT RACE or SNAIL RACE for some future date. Each participant furnishes his own racer. Confine the racers at the center of a large circle (small, for snails). Lift the cover at the word "Go". First to cross the circumference line wins. This is a good interest creator but, of course, some rules are needed.

---

*See "Directions for Collecting and Mounting Insects", in **How to Know the Insects,** Jaques.

48. If you live within reach of the sea coast make a collection of *MARINE SHELLS*.

49. Use living Planaria or Earth Worms to demonstrate *REGENERATION*.

Figure 6

50. A *CARROT* may be partly hollowed out so as to hold water when suspended by the "tail". If hung in a window and kept filled with water it is soon surrounded by a growth of up-turning feathery leaves. Fig. 6.

51. *SWEET POTATOES* may be grown in the same way but the vine trails in this instance.

52. During the warmer months a *SWARM OF BEES* may be kept in a glass walled hive in the laboratory to the interest of many.

53. Take your students on frequent *FIELD TRIPS*. If you are not permitted to go at regular laboratory hours, go with the more interested ones at other times. A field trip should be for serious study and not be a hilarious hike.

54. Study *APHIDS* in relation to the *ANTS*. With a little care both can be moved indoors.

55. In studying *PLANTS* do not neglect the *CULTIVATED* ones. A knowledge of both the ornamentals and of the garden plants is important.

56. Start a long time project of radically changing or improving some *PLANT*. Milkweeds, for instance, would seem to have just as good possibilities for ornamentals as Gladiolus or Dahlias.

57. Make a study of *FEATHERS;* — their structure and their coloration.

58. When an animal or plant has been determined by use of a key, then make a *LIST* of the *ESSENTIAL CHARACTERS* used in each step of the key. This makes a highly critical description of the order, family or species.

59. Make a *TREE CENSUS* of your town, or some part of your town, so that when finished it can be told how many different species of trees and how many specimens of each are found in your area.

60. Make a named collection of *WINTER TWIGS*. Be careful not to mutilate the trees from which the twigs are taken.

61. *GRAFTING* and *BUDDING* of closely related plants are relatively easy. Try some unusual species.

62. A Microscopic Study of the *HAIRS* of different animals is interesting.

7

63. Most regions have many CRUSTACEANS. Collect living or museum specimens.

64. Make a collection of TREE LEAVES. These can be mounted between two pieces of glass for laboratory study.

65. REPEAT some of MENDEL'S EXPERIMENTS with either plants or animals.

66. Many ALGAE can be grown indefinitely in small covered aquaria in a favorably lighted place.

67. Samples of WOOD make an important collection.

68. Many nature lovers in our country and abroad are glad to EXCHANGE SPECIMENS in the groups in which they are interested. (See the Naturalist's Directory).

69. Collect INSECT COCOONS and other PUPAE and permit them to emerge indoors.

70. A MINIATURE FOREST may be grown in a shallow dish with moss and lichens for vegetation and perhaps a few small ferns for trees.

71. Make a collection of MOSSES. They are fairly easily identified and may be mounted on cards or kept in envelopes.*

72. LICHENS may be collected and mounted by gluing to the bottoms of shallow boxes or trays.

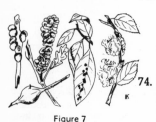

Figure 7

73. SLIME MOLDS likewise may be glued to the inside of the lids of paper pill boxes. The delicate slime molds are protected in the box. When studying them the box lids make easy the handling of the specimen.

74. INSECT GALLS are often abundant on plants. They may be collected for the galls alone or confined in containers until the insects growing in them come out. Fig. 7.

75. MAPS of a town or region locating good collecting grounds, or showing where rare plants are found make valuable teaching aids. Constructing such maps is a good student project.

76. When the leaves are off of the trees in the winter, the hanging NESTS made by the BALTIMORE ORIOLE may be readily located. A CENSUS count of these nests in a community permits a close estimate of the number of nesting pairs of Baltimore Orioles in that region the previous summer.

77. If this information (76) shows the species of tree in each case and is compared with a tree census of the same region, some interesting facts about TREE PREFERENCES of these birds are revealed.

---

*See **How to Know the Mosses,** Conard.

78. A search and record of the different species of *AMPHIBIA* in a region would be profitable.

79. *INSECT COLLECTING CONTESTS* are profitable in getting students to observe closely. Many of the best records in the Iowa Insect Survey have been gotten this way.

80. An effort to make the largest possible list of *PLANT AND ANIMAL ORDERS*, for which one could locate representatives in his region would be good. The list in the back of this book could be checked for the record.

81. Try *CROSSING* closely related species of *PLANTS* and carry the hybrids to two generations to get many varieties.

82. In teaching the use of identification keys, good *PICTURES* or *CHARTS* may be substituted for actual animals and plants. Try it with these keys.

83. *INSECTIVOROUS PLANTS* may be grown in a miniature swamp in a covered aquarium. These plants are always of interest.

84. *OWLS* live largely on rodents. The undigested skulls are regurgitated. By examining the pellets under an owl roost a list of the food animals of these owls may be worked out.

85. A *COMPARITIVE STUDY* of the common and red seeded dandelions of the campus one Spring was found profitable. A search was made for constant differences other than seed color, by which the two species could be distinguished, and the relative abundance, relative prolificacy and times of flowering were studied.

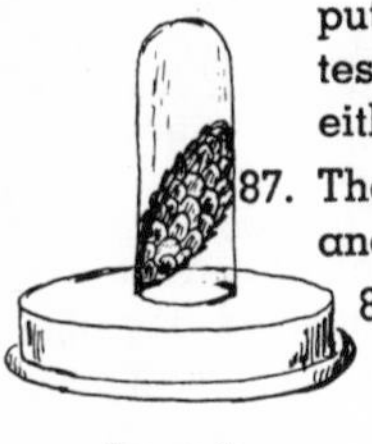

86. *DELICATE OBJECTS* may be permanently mounted by putting the object in a test tube and then fixing the test tube in a plaster base. This may be used for either wet or dry mounts. Fig. 8.

87. There are many interesting *FUNGI*. Their collecting and study should be profitable.

Figure 8

88. A *FLOWER COLLECTING CONTEST* may be made highly important. The first three students to bring a new flower are given 5, 3 and 1 points respectively. The plants are recorded with dates on a list on the wall. The flower is left in a jar of water kept for that purpose. The student having the highest total of points at the announced closing date wins. In our region the list includes from 300 to 500 species of flowering plants each spring by June 1st. The lists should be kept, as very interesting data are to be had from them. We now have such lists covering a period of 35 years. Students should be taught to get these specimens without destroying the plant.

89. Rearing *LIFE HISTORIES OF INSECTS*, proves fascinating to many students and is always profitable. Natural conditions should be imitated to insure success.

90. Attempts to rear insects on changed food plants often reveals some interesting facts.

91. Aquaria with *NATIVE FISH* are interesting.

92. If a Fly or Cock Roach is permitted to walk across the sterile agar in a petri dish and the dish incubated for 48 hours, the tracks are plainly portrayed by the growths of *BACTERIA*.

93. Catch a *BIRD* with *MUDDY FEET*, remove the *SOIL* and plant it in a pot of sterile soil. Many plants may often be raised this way, telling something about plant dissemination over long distances.

94. Cartoonists and jouralists sometimes display their *IGNORANCE OF BIOLOGY*. A call for *CARTOONS* or *CLIPPINGS* with such blunders will keep students biologically conscious in their general reading.

95. *BIRD PICTURES* make a rather ideal method of beginning to teach bird identification. Make a collection of bird pictures.

96. Keep *TADPOLES* and small *FISH* in an aqarium with *AQUATIC INSECTS*. Record the daily loss of fish and tadpoles.

97. See that *COLLECTIONS* are neat, orderly and *ACCURATELY LABELED*. Occasionally school collections are only a bunch of junk and as such are worse than worthless.

98. Leave cans of water exposed in different places and record the number of *MOSQUITO LARVA* developing in them.

99. How far may *HOUSE FLIES TRAVEL*? Devise a way to find out.

100. At what rate of *SPEED* do *INSECTS* fly?. Some coordinated work with the Physics Department might answer this query.

101. Encourage your students to *ASK IMPORTANT QUESTIONS*; then devise research methods for answering them.

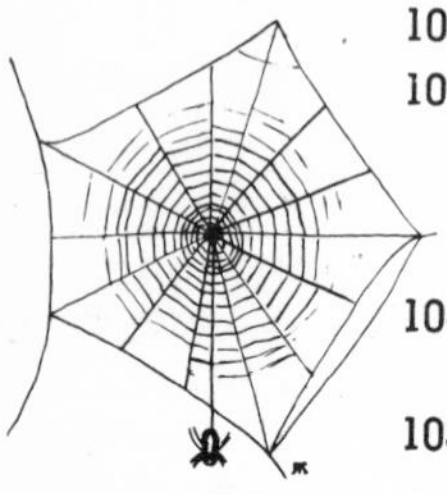

Figure 9

102. Study *SPIDERS* in field or laboratory.

103. Make a *COLLECTION OF SPIDERS* to see how many apparently different ones occur in your region. (They must be kept in preservative; — not pinned like insects).

104. Photograph different types of *SPIDERS WEBS*. (Fig. 9).

105. *PROTOZOAN CULTURES* may be reared in small glass containers. They prove fascinating to many students. Get water for these from as many outside sources as possible.

106. Many insects may be kept alive in captivity. An *INSECT ZOO* project should be helpful.

107. Teach *CONSERVATION* but do not be "silly" about it. To spend a lot of energy and money to raise a brood of wild birds so that they may be wiped out by one blast of a shot gun, or to forbid the Botany Class to pick flowers for their herbariums and two weeks later turn in a hundred sheep or tear up the whole region with some construction project, seems plainly dumb. True conservation is loving plants and animals so sincerely that we want to see them succeed in their place at all times.

108. If it is springtime, determine which trees of an area produce their *FLOWERS* before the *LEAVES*, which with the leaves and which ones after the leaves have matured.

109. Your region likely has some places where *FOSSIL* bearing rock strata are exposed. Take your class there; see how many species of fossils they can find. Determine the geological age to which the exposure belongs.

110. Make a collection of *SINGING INSECTS*; keep them in comfortable living quarters and observe their type of musical instruments. A further study of the influences of temperature, light and other ecological factors on the singing should prove worth doing.

111. Have your students make mounts of the different types of legs and wings of insects. Reward in some way the makers of the best displays.

112. Some neatly made skeleton mounts of legs, wings and fins of some vertebrates to *SHOW HOMOLOGY* would be very useful in teaching. The students making the mounts would learn much, too.

113. Take a square foot of *SOIL* to a depth of 6 inches from a garden, pasture, roadside, playground, etc. Spread the soil in shallow pans. Maintain favorable conditions for germination to find how many young plants grow on it and how many different species are represented. Identify the plants if possible.

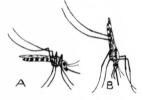

Figure 9½. Mosquitos at rest or preparing to bite. A, **Culex** B, **Anopheles**

114. After a discussion of the human diseases borne by *MOSQUITOS*, organize and conduct a survey to determine the percentage of *ANOPHELES* among the mosquitos of your region.

115. Good *NATURE ARTISTS* are always in demand. Perhaps you have some student with talent in this line who needs encouragement.

116. Encourage your students to *DEVISE* and suggest little *RESEARCH PROJECTS* to determine some new facts about the out-of-doors. Initiative and resourcefulness should be encouraged in every way possible.

117. A colony of *BUMBLEBEES* may be secured (tricky job) and brought indoors for study in a glass walled hive (which should be kept darkened except when being observed). The runway to the exterior of the building permitting them to go and come at will should not open too close to outdoor walks, for obvious reasons.

SOME HELPFUL REFERENCE BOOKS

"O F the making of many books, there is no end." The large number of painstakingly written and beautifully illustrated nature books indicates a great general interest in Living Things. In the hope that it may be helpful, a small list of some excellent reference books follows. The list is almost wholly confined to the manuals which make possible the naming of species within the group considered. There are many valuable texts on Biology, Botany and Zoology, or more specialized fields, that should be helpful. No effort has been made to include these.

GENERAL

"The Living World", S. H. Williams

"Fresh Water Biology", Ward & Whipple

PLANTS

"The Fresh-water Algae of the United States", G. M. Smith

"One Thousand American Fungi", Chas. McIlvaine

"The Fungi which Cause Plant Disease", F. L. Stevens

"The Mushroom Book", N. L. Marshall

"How to Know the Trees", H. E. Jaques

"How to Know the Mosses", H. S. Conard

"Plants We Eat and Wear", H. E. Jaques

"Mosses with Hand-lens and Microscope", A. J. Grout

"Illustrated Flora of the Northern United States and Canada", Britton & Brown

"Illustrated Flora of the Pacific States", Abrams

"Manual of Botany", 7th Edition, Asa Gray

"Field Book of American Wild Flowers", F. Schuyler Mathews

"Manual of Cultivated Plants", L. H. Bailey

"Flora of the Southeastern United States", Small

"Flora of the Rocky Mountains", P. A. Rydberg

"Field Book of Western Wild Flowers", Armstrong

"Wild Flowers of California", M. E. Parsons

"Plants of Central Iowa", H. S. Conard

"Plant Families — How to Know Them", H. E. Jaques

"How to Know the Spring Flowers", M. J. Cuthbert

"Weeds of Lawn and Garden", J. M. Fogg, Jr.

"Field Book of American Trees and Shrubs", M. F. Schuyler

"Handbook of the Trees of the Eastern United States", R. B. Hough

"Trees and Shrubs of the Rocky Mountains", Burton O. Longyear

ANIMALS

"Cambridge Natural History"
"The Parade of the Animal King-
dom", R. W. Hegner
"American Natural History",
Wm. T. Hornaday
"A Manual of the Common Inver-
tebrate Animals, except Insects",
H. S. Pratt
"A Manual of the Land and
Freshwater Vertebrates of the
United States", H. S. Pratt
"Manual of the Vertebrates",
David Starr Jordan
"Culture Methods for Inverte-
brates", Needham
"Handbook of Protozoology",
Richard R. Kudo
"The Shell Book", Mary C.
Dickerson
"An Introduction to Entomology",
J. H. Comstock
"American Insects", V. L. Kellogg
"Field Book of Insects",
Frank E. Lutz
"How to Know the Insects",
H. E. Jaques
"The Insects", L. O. Howard
"The Butterfly Book",
W. J. Holland
"The Moth Book", W. J. Holland
"Ants", W. M. Wheeler

"The Spider Book",
J. H. Comstock
"Manual of External Parasites",
H. E. Ewing
"The Book of Fishes", National
Geographic Society
"American Food and Game
Fishes", Jordan & Evermann
"The Frog Book", Mary C.
Dickerson
"The Reptile Book", R. L. Ditmars
"Snakes of the World"
R. L. Ditmars
"Handbook of the Birds of East-
ern North America", Frank
M. Chapman
"Birds of New York State",
E. W. Nelson
"Handbook of Birds of Western
United States", F. M. Bailey
"A Field Guide to Western
Birds", R. T. Peterson
"A Field Guide to the Birds",
R. T. Peterson
"Field Book of North American
Mammals", H. E. Anthony
"Wild Animals of N. America",
E. W. Nelson
"The Mammals of Eastern U. S."
W. J. Hamilton, Jr.

HOW TO USE THE KEYS

 YSTEMATIC Biology is a problem or arranging plants and animals in some orderly fashion and then knowing on which "shelf" to look for the ones in question. This identification or determination is most readily done by means of keys, which divide the group under consideration into two parts, each of which is divided again and again until the desired determination has been reached. Illustrations help greatly in making the meaning of key statements clearer.

All living things are either plants or animals. To which one of these two groups a large percentage of living things would belong is usually obvious. A key to help with the less evident cases appears on page 16. It will be noted that the plant part of the illustrated key is printed on green tinted pages, while the animal section is brown tinted. This permits the user to open at once to the desired section of the book.

Suppose Fred's uncle mails him an interesting shell-covered creature with five slim twisted arms, and that Fred, or his teacher, wishes to find what it is. They feel sure it is an animal but begin by comparing 1a with 1b an page 16 and find that they are right in placing it in the Animal Kingdom. Turning to the beginning of the peach section (p. 57) and comparing 1a with 1b they see that its size and structure make it a Metazoan under 1b. At the right a "2" appears which means that they must next compare 2a with 2b. Because of its radial symmetry they see that their specimen falls under 2a and that they are referred to 3. 3a will not fit the case but 3b does, showing that it belongs to the Phylum Echinodermata. They are now referred to page 84 and start in under "Key to the Classes and Orders of the Phylum Echinodermata". 1a plainly fits the conditions as does also 2b. Since

14

the arms of their specimen are "without a groove" they decide that it belongs to the class *Ophiuroidea*. By comparing 6a with 6b their attention is called to the fact that its arms are unbranched and they know then that Fred's uncle sent him a "Brittle Star", belonging to the Order *Ophiurae*. Now if Fred's teacher will ask him to make a list of all the characters mentioned in the key statements he selected, he will have an excellent description of a Brittle Star.

Other animals and plants may be run through the keys in this same way. A large percentage of the recognized orders are included. To make the keys easier to handle some small orders of uncommon Living Things have been purposely omitted. A complete list of orders is found in the back of the book. Orders are further divided into families; families into genera and genera into species. Of course, to attempt to go into these finer divisions with these keys would make the book unwieldy in size and prohibitive in cost. Many excellent books are already in existence which treat special groups of plants and animals. The logical next step is to refer to the right one of them.

Most of the unusual terms are explained in the keys; others are defined in the index-glossary.

PICTURED-KEYS TO THE PHYLA, CLASSES AND ORDERS OF ALL LIVING THINGS

THERE are two great groups of living things, the Animal Kingdom and the Plant Kingdom. To the novice it might seem that any suggestion for telling these two groups apart would be wholly needless. To place many living things in the proper one of these two kingdoms is not always as simple as it may appear. Scientists, after many years of study, are not agreed on the relationship of some species of living things. The key that follows should be helpful but cannot settle all cases.

1a Has the power of locomotion; responds quickly to external stimuli. Form of body highly diverse but usually the same for all members of each species. Size, highly variable but quite constant for each species. Organs compact and mostly internal.

(In some cases the organism is attached or has no self locomotion, but these all require organic food.) Fig. 10.

THE ANIMAL KINGDOM

Turn to the peach colored portion of the book, beginning with page 57.

Figure 10

1b Does not respond quickly to external stimuli; has no power of locomotion (except in special cases); the form of the body is rather variable; often wide diversity of size in same species; new organs are added externally.

(Some plants are free swimming, but they are usually green in color and live on inorganic substances.) Fig. 11.

THE PLANT KINGDOM

Turn to the green colored portion of the book beginning with page 17.

Figure 11

16

KEY TO THE PRINCIPAL GROUPS
OF THE PLANT KINGDOM

The plants are usually divided into four great groups. It is commonly recognized that some of these groups are "artificial". The Thallophyta in particular includes many plants which are somewhat alike in their simplicity but which are evidently widely disrelated.

1a Plants without distinction of root, stem and leaf; without flowers, (green forms, mostly aquatic); fungi, both aquatic and terrestrial; lichens, etc. *"Have No Archegonia"*. Division THALLOPHYTA p. 17

1b Plants with distinct leaves; with or without roots or flowers 2

2a Small plants (to 4 or 5 inches tall) with green or gray-green leaves, or tiny leaf-like forms on damp earth or floating on water. No true roots or flowers.
(Some small oval green discs floating on quiet water with roots suspended beneath are flowering plants and do not belong here.) *"Have Archegonia But No Vascular Bundles"*. (Mosses and Liverworts.) Figs. 70 to 78. ....Phylum BRYOPHYTA p. 37

2b Plants with true roots and vascular bundles; mostly with veiny leaves. 3

3a Plants without flowers or seeds, herbs (not woody), propagated by spores, Figs. 79, 80 and 81. *"Have Vascular Bundles But No Seeds"*. (The Ferns, etc.) ....Phylum PTERIDOPHYTA p. 40

3b Plants with flowers (sometimes very simple; one tiny stamen or one pistil may constitute a flower) and seeds. *"Have Seeds"*. Figs. 82 to 139. (The seed bearing plants.)
Phylum SPERMATOPHYTA p. 41

KEY TO THE PHYLA CLASSES AND ORDERS
OF THE DIVISION THALLOPHYTA

1a Plants green, with chlorophyll, thus organizing their own food by photosynthesis. Figs. 13 to 38. 2
Sub-division PHYCOPHYTA, The Algae

1b Plants without chlorophyll (not green). Living parasitically on living plants or animals or as saprophytes on dead, organic matter. Figs. 39 to 69. ....Sub-division MYCOPHYTA, The Fungi p. 27

1c Dual organisms in which a green plant species (alga) is held in parasitic embrace by a species of fungus. Usually gray-green or yellow-green but sometimes displaying bright colors. Common on tree trunks, rocks and often growing directly in the ground. (The Lichens.)

Figure 12

Fig. 12. a, *Physcia* sp.;
   b, *Cladonia* sp.
The Lichens are soil builders. There are three types; Crustaceous, with poorly defined mycelia, often on rocks; Foliaceous, flat and leaf-like, and Fruticose, bushy and erect or hanging.

The fungal plant is almost always an Ascomycete (see p. 31) and frequently produces apothecia and asci for reproduction (one or two species are Basidiomycetes). Many lichens also release very tiny balls each containing a few algal plants wrapped in fungal threads. These soredia are carried by the wind or water and develop into new plants.

2a Plant cells without recognizable nucleus or plastids. Coloring matter (usually blue-green) diffused throughout the cell.
Figs. 13 and 14. (The Blue-Green Algae). 3
Class MYXOPHYCEAE (Cyanophyceae)

The general blue-green shade of these simple plants is a sufficient character for their ready recognition. Many species also contain a red pigment which at times may become the dominant color. The Red Sea seems to owe its name to this fact. The "blue-greens" have a way of developing with amazing rapidity in sewage polluted waters, and decompose to lift an odor to high-heaven in a way that has taken the profit out of many summer resorts.

2b Not as in 2a. Plant cells with distinct plastids and of various colors and shapes. 4

3a Unicellular or colonial in habit; never forming filaments. Reproduction vegetative only. . . . . .Order CHROOCOCCALES

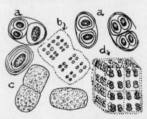

Figure 13

Fig. 13. a, *Gleocapsa*, dividing irregularly; b, *Merismopedia*, dividing in two planes to form a plate; c, *Synechococcus*, dividing in one plane to form a chain; d, *Eucapsis*, dividing in three planes to form a cube.
The blue-green algae and the bacteria seem to have much in common. This overlapping of characters makes it difficult to definitely place many species.

3b Cells forming definite filaments. . . . . .Order HORMOGONALES

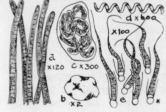

Figure 14

Fig. 14. a, *Oscillatoria*; b, nodule of *Nostoc*; c, filaments of *Nostoc*; d, *Spirulina*; e, *Rivularia*.
Most of the plants of this order have an occasional clear cell (heterocyst) that aids in reproduction. Some species of the order are found on damp ground; others are purely aquatic.

18

4a Algae that are bright "grass-green" in color. Figs. 15 to 23. 5

4b Algae with red, brown or yellow pigments more or less masking the green chlorophyll. Figs. 24 to 38. 12

5a Plant fine; relatively small. Figs. 16 to 23. 6

5b Plant coarse, at least a few inches long, branched, with nodes from which arise whorls of cylindrical leaves which in turn bear leaflets; sometimes encrusted with lime. ......Phylum **CHAROPHYTA**
Order **CHARALES**

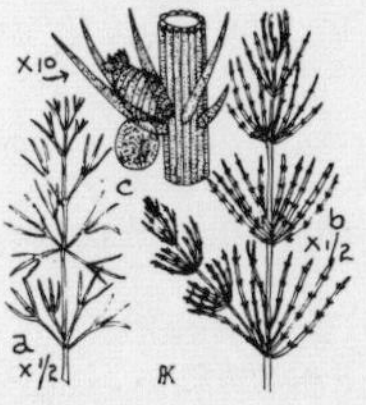

Fig. 15. a, branch of *Nitella;* b, small branch of *Chara;* c, portion of lateral stem, antheridia (male) and oogonia (female organs).

Figure 15

6a Naked free swimming cells with one, two or rarely more whip-like flagella at the anterior end. Some species are colonial. (Some have a non-motile encysted stage.) Sexual reproduction unknown. Fig. 14b. ....Phylum **EUGLENAPHYCEAE**
Order **EUGLENALES**

These living things are on the border line between the plants and the animals. Many of them are claimed by the zoologists so the reader is referred to page 61 in the animal kingdom.

6b Microscopic single celled plants, to large thallus like plants with cellulose walls. The flagella of motile forms usually number 2 or 4 and are equal in length. Most species of the phylum have sexual reproduction. Figs. 16 to 23 7
Phylum **CHLOROPHYTA**

There is but one class, the Chlorophyceae, but it is so large as to include more fresh water species than all the other fresh water algae taken together.

7a Plants definitely cellular in structure. One or more cells. Figs. 17 to 23. 8

7b Plants comparatively large, with many nuclei but with no cross walls or definite cells. Filaments branched. ...Order **SIPHONALES**

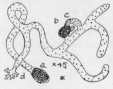

Fig. 16. Filament of *Vaucheria.* a, Zoospore; b, Oogonium; c, Antheridium; d, Hold fast.
This plant is often found making green felt-like patches on damp ground. Under green house benches is a good place to look for it. Several other species grow in water.

Figure 16

19

8a Vegetative cells motile by means of flagella (some have non-motile resting periods). Order VOLVOCALES

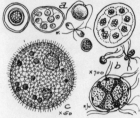

Fig. 17. a, *Clamydomonas*, several stages: b, *Pandorina*, several stages; c. *Volvox*, forming new colonies within the sphere.

Volvox colonies have from 500 to several thousand cells, and are large enough to be seen by the unaided eye. *V. globator*, is our most common species.

Figure 17

8b Vegetative cells not self-moving. Reproductive cells often motile..9

9a Usually spherical or ovoid cells held together in colonies by a gelatinous secretion in which the cells are embedded. These gelatinous colonies take various shapes and sizes.
Order TETRASPORALES

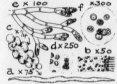

Fig. 18. a, Colony; b, Cross section of *Tetraspora cylindrica*; c, Colony; d, cross section of *Tetraspora lubrica*; e, *Prasinocladus*; f, *Sphaerocystis*.

Figure 18

These plants are often abundant in our lakes. Some species grow attached to larger algae and others float free in the water. Still other species are found in damp places out of water.

9b Plants not forming gelatinous colonies. (A few members of the Chlorococcales are an exception). Figs. 19 to 23 10

10a Single celled plants or multicellular colonies, but never forming filaments. (The water net (Fig. 19f) is not a true filament). The cells take many unusual shapes. (A few colonies are embedded in a gelatinous mass; and another few expanding into a thallus).
Order CHLOROCOCCALES

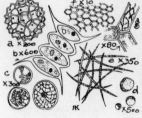

Fig. 19. a, *Pediastrum* (the "Rotary" plant); b, *Scenedesmus*; c, *Chlorococcum*; d, *Chlorella*; e, *Ankistrodesmus*; f, *Hydrodictyon* (portion of net); g, parts of three cells.

The nets of *Hydrodictyon* may attain a length of 6 to 10 inches. There are two species. It is found in pools of quiet water.

Figure 19

20

10b Plants highly multicellular, leaf-like or developing into hollow tubes or solid cylinders. **Order ULVALES**

Fig. 20. a, *Enteromorpha;* b, *Ulva* or Sea Lettuce; c, cellular structure.

The members of this order are mostly salt water forms. A few species grow in highly concentrated brine lakes.

Figure 20

10c Not as in 10a or 10b but developing into a branched or unbranched filament. Figs. 21 to 23. 11

11a Zoospores and male reproductive cells with a ring of many flagella at apical end. With apical caps indicating where cell division has occurred. Filaments simple or branched. **Order OEDOGONIALES**

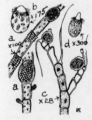

Fig. 21. a, filaments of *Oedogonium;* b, Zoospore; c, filament of *Bulbochaete;* d, Zoospore.
Oedogonium is always aquatic. More than 200 species are known in our country.

Figure 21

11b Zoospores with two or four flagella. Filament simple or branched (only a singular spherical cell or irregular colony of such cells in *Protococcus (c).* **Order ULOTRICHALES**

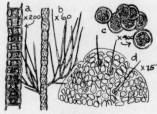

Fig. 22. a, *Ulothrix;* b, *Draparnaldia;* c, *Protococcus;* d, *Coleochaete.*
Everyone should know *Protococcus.* It is found on the shaded side of trees, fences, stones, etc., in damp locations and is one of our most common algae.

Figure 22

11c No zoospores. No flagellated reproductive spores. Reproduction by a zygospore formed by the union of two non-motile cells. Filament always unbranched.　　　　　Order ZYGNEMOTALES

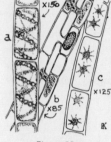

Fig. 23. a, Spirogyra, portion of vegetative filament; b, Spirogyra conpugating; c, Zygnema.
The spiral bands in each cell of Spirogyra give it its name. This plant may often be recognized in the field by its slipperiness.

Figure 23

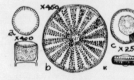

Fig. 24. a, Orthosira; b, Stephanodiscus; c, Cyclotella.
These are fresh-water species. While widely distributed throughout our country, members of this order are not nearly so common as in the following order.

Figure 24

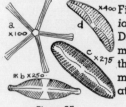

Fig. 25. a, Asterionella; b, Stauroneis; c, Pinnularia; d, Amphora.
Diatoms may be found in the slimy bottoms of almost any water course or mud puddle. Examine them with a compound microscope. Their movements and the markings of their shells command attention.

Figure 25　　　　　　22

15a Motile cells with flagella inserted in a transverse furrow; one
flagellum wraps around the cell transversely; the other extends
vertically backward. Contents of organism golden brown or colorless. **Class DIANOPHYCEAE**
(This group is considered more animal like than plant like). For
its further classification, see Order Dianoflagellida under the
Protozoa, p. 60.

15b Plants without a transverse groove 16

16a Motile cells with two unequal flagella at anterior end. Discoid
chromatophores yellowish green; without pyrenoids; stored food
oil, - not starch. The cell walls of many species are made of H
shaped pieces which overlap. Figs. 27 to 29 17
Class HETEROKONTAE

16b Motile cells with one or two flagella at the anterior end; when two
they may be either equal or unequal in length. Chromatophores
are a distinctive golden brown. **Class CHRYSOPHYCEAE**
With vegetative cells motile and but temporarily amoeboid.
Order CHRYSOMONADALES

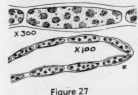

Fig. 26. a, *Synura*; b, *Dinobryon*. (2 species)
Dinobryon is a large genus containing both
colonial and solitary attached species, and
still other free-swimming solitary forms.

Figure 26

17a **Cells arranged in filaments.** **Order HETEROTRICHALES**

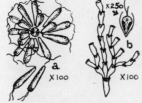

Fig. 27. *Tribonema*, parts of filament.
Most of the members of this order have unbranched filaments. They are found among
the other algae of rivers, lakes and pools.
One family has branched filaments. Its members grow on damp soil.

Figure 27

17b **Plants with bulb like multinucleate head and branching root-like
parts, growing in soil.** **Order HETEROSIPHONALES**
(This order contains but one genus and it, but one important
species, the one here pictured and described.)

Fig. 28. *Botrydium granulatum*.
These plants sometimes grow very abundantly on
drying soils that have been smoothed out by rain.
They appear as tiny gray-green balls and usually
cover the soil when growing conditions are favorable.

Figure 28

17c Not like either 17a or 17b. Usually single celled.

Order HETEROCOCCALES

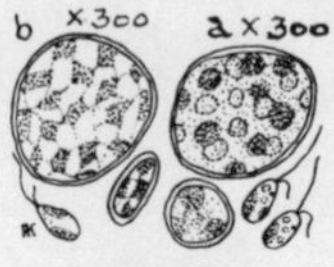

Figure 29

Fig. 29. a, *Botrydiopsis;* b, *Leuvenia.*
These tiny plants are found in pools and on damp ground, and are frequently mixed with larger species such as *Vaucheria.*

KEY TO THE MORE IMPORTANT ORDERS OF THE PHYLUM PHAEOPHYTA (Brown Algae)

18a Having alternation of generations (plants reproducing by sexual methods alternating with plants that reproduce asexually). Figs. 31 to 34 19

18b Plants with no apparent alternation or generations. Medium sized, with flattened leaf-like branches. Large non-motile eggs. Very small flagellated sperms. (The rock weeds).

Order FUCALES

Figure 30

Fig. 30. a, *Fucus vesiculosus;* b, *Sargassum.*
This is a very large order of over 300 marine plants. They are found in all the oceans. Most of the species are attached to rocks though several species of *Sargassum* are free floating.

19a Asexual and sexual plants similar in size and general appearance. Figs. 31 and 32 20

19b Asexual and sexual plants plainly differing in size and appearance. Figs. 33 and 34 21

20a Most species of fine thread-like parts, much branched. Asexual plants producing pear shaped "swarm spores" each bearing two flagella on one side. Sexual plants producing similar gametes (sex cells) each with two lateral flagella. These gamates unite and develop into an asexual plant. Order ECTOCARPALES

Figure 31

Fig. 31. *Ectocarpus;* a, branch of a filament with sporangia; b, swarm spores.
These marine algae are abundant along our Atlantic coast and are also found on our Pacific coast but less abundantly. The fine, much branched plants grow attached to larger algae.

24

RED ALGAE

20b **Moderate sized plants; most species with branching flattened leaf-like parts. Asexual plants producing large non-motile spores in groups of four. Female plants producing large non-motile eggs in single celled oogonia on surface of thallus. Male plants producing immense numbers of flagellated spermatozoids in antheridia on surface of thallus.** Order DICTYOTALES

Fig. 32. *Dictyota dicotyma;* a, typical plant; b, tetraspore (asexual); c, fruiting body with antheridia; d, a group of oogonia.

These marine plants (about 100 species) require warm water for successful growth. They are found along our South-east and California shores and are very abundant in tropical seas.

Figure 32

21a **Asexual plants very small; bearing numerous biflagellated zoospores. Female plants moderate sized with flattened branching parts bearing comparatively large biflagellated gametes. Male plants (similar in appearance to female) bearing much smaller biflagellated gametes.** Order CUTLERIALES

Fig. 33. *Cutleria multifida;* a, sexual plant with female and male gametes (b); c, asexual plant; d, zoospore.

These plants of which there are but two genera grow in the Mediterranean and other warm European waters. They are scantily found along the Florida coast.

Figure 33

21b **Asexual plant very large and heavy with broad leaf-like parts often attached to a float and a long cord; some tree-like. It bears numerous biflagellated zoospores on surface of thallus. These develop into mocroscopic male and female plants which bear motile sperms and large non-motile eggs, respectively. (The Kelps).** Order LAMINARIALES

Fig. 34. "The Devil's Apron"... *Laminaria saccharina;* a, plants with hold fasts for attachment.

The truly "big boys" of the Thallophyta belong in this order. Several of the more than 100 species may reach a length of 50 to 100 feet of over. Found in both of our oceans they are more abundant and larger in the Pacific. These and other large brown algae are known as kelps and are a source of Iodine.

Figure 34

KEY TO THE MORE COMMON ORDERS OF THE PHYLUM RHODOPHYCEAE

22a Branched or unbranched filaments or flat thalli; but one cell in thickness. Cells with large stellate chromatophores. Filaments with continuous gelatinous wall. Asexual reproduction by naked non-flagellated spores; sexual reproduction simple.

Order BANGIALES

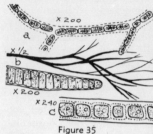

Fig. 35. *Asterocystis,* part of filament; b, *Compsopogon,* part of thallus and one branch enlarged; c, *Bangia,* part of thallus. The species here pictured are fresh-water forms. *Porphyra,* a marine genus with several known species is a broadly expanded red thallus which may attain a length of five feet or more. It is an important food in the Orient and in parts of Europe.

Figure 35

22b Not as above. 23

23a Simple plants with no asexual reproduction. Carpogonia (female reproductive organs) at end of branches. (Most of the fresh water species of red algae belong here.)   Order NEMALIONALES

Fig. 36. *Batrachospermum;* a, a branch; b, single filament; c, *Tuomeya.*
These two species are fresh-water forms. *Nemalion* is a marine genus frequently used for laboratory study.

Figure 36

23b Not as in 23a. Figs. 37 and 38 24

24a Mostly of comparatively large size and coarse, tough texture. The undivided carpogonium develops into spores. The tetraspores are usually buried in the thallus and the antheridia borne in surface patches of small cells.   Order GIGARTINALES

Fig. 37. *Chondrus crispus.* A plant showing habit of growth.
This plant grows in abundance off the European coast where it is known as Irish moss and is used for food. *Iridaea* is a Pacific coast genus producing a broad thallus.

Figure 37

24b Carpogonium after fertilization divides into two cells which forms two masses of spores. The largest order of red algae.

Order CERAMIALES

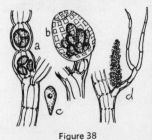

Figure 38

Fig. 38. *Polysiphonia;* a, branch with tetraspores; b, carpospores within a cystocarp; c, a single carpospore; d, branch bearing an antheridium.

This highly interesting plant grows in great abundance along the Atlantic coast, masses of several species often being attached to *Fucus.* The order is not so well represented in the Pacific.

KEY TO THE PHYLA AND MORE COMMON ORDERS OF THE SUB-DIVISION MYCOPHYTA
(The Fungi)

1a Vegetative body, a plasmodium (naked slimy mass of living substance flowing in decaying wood, leaves, etc., usually in the dark). Reproductive bodies, tiny knob or plume-like structures (sporangia) usually in groups and of various colors. Figs. 39 and 43 to 45. (The Slime Molds). 5

Phylum MYXOTHALLOPHYTA

Figure 39

Fig. 39. Some typical slime molds.
These organisms are sometimes claimed by the zoologists because of the amoeboid nature of the swarm spores and plasmodium. The tiny sporangia here pictured are often bright colored and very attractive.

1b Not as in 1a. 2

2a Microscopic single celled plants (often clinging in groups or chains). Reproduction by dividing through middle (fission). Figs. 40 to 42. (The Bacteria) 3

Phylum SCHIZOMYCETES

Bacteria include the smallest known living things. Some are so minute that 50,000 of these tiny plants would need to be placed edge to edge to make a row an inch in length.* A cubic inch measure once filled could hold enough typhoid bacilla (a fairly large species of bacteria) to furnish more than 3000 of these deadly germs to every man, woman and child now living on the earth.

It should be borne in mind that while many of our worst diseases are due to bacteria, many other species are highly useful.

---

*There are many evidences of "LOWER BACTERIA" which are too small to be seen by the compound microscope. Filterable Viruses would fall under this heading.

2b Fungi with vegetative body of filaments and various reproductive organs. Figs. 46 to 69. (The True Fungi). 7

Phylum EUMYCETES

3a Bacteria with cells, spherical in form. (May be solitary or clinging together in filaments, plates or masses.) Fig. 40.

COCCI**

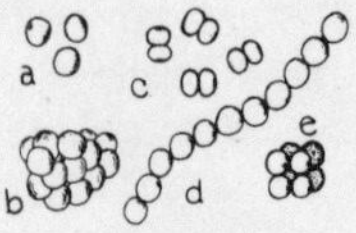

Figure 40

Fig. 40. These spherical bacteria may be separated, as *single cells* (a micrococcus); clinging in irregular masses (b, staphylococcus); remain in pairs (c, diplococcus); form chains (d, streptococcus) or form masses taking the shape of cubes (e, sarcina).

The bacteria producing spinal meningitis, gonorrhoeae, and pneumonia, for instance, belong here.

3b Cells not spherical. Figs. 41 and 42. 4

4a Cells straight rods. BACILLI

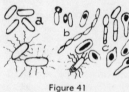

Figure 41

Fig. 41. These cylindrical species may be divided into three groups;—
a, *Bacterium*, rod-shaped cells producing no endospores (spore within the cell); b, *Bacillus*, cells forming endospores, aerobic; c, *Clostridium*,-cells frequently enlarged in spore formation, anaerobic. The organisms causing tuberculosis and typhoid and the ones that sour milk belong in this group.

4b Cells spiral. SPIRILLI, ETC.

Figure 42

Fig. 42. These spiral species may be divided into three groups;—
a, *Microspira*,-short rods, slightly bent; b, *Spirillum*,-long rigid, curved or spiral-shaped cells; c, *Spirochaetea*, long flexible spiral shaped cells. The organisms causing Trench Mouth, Asiatic cholera and Syphillis are examples.

**It will be noted that a much more elaborate classification of bacteria is given in the table of Phyla and Orders (p. 133). The arrangement used there is a modification by Bergey of the classification recognized by the American Society of Bacteriologists. Since the structural characters of bacteria have but scant use in classification it has been thought best to give only this rough separation of a few very common forms here.

KEY TO THE SUBCLASSES OF THE PHYLUM
MYXOTHALLOPHYTA (Slime Molds)

5a Parasites in the cells of living plants.

Class PHYTOMYXINAE
Order PLASMODIOPHORALES

Fig. 43. *Plasmodiophora brassicae.* A cabbage root infected with this disease. This is the cause of the common club root or cabbage and some related plants. The plasmodium living within the root cells of the host produces gall formations. Only a few species of this group are known.

Figure 43

5b Saprophytes living in decaying vegetable matter.
Figs. 44 and 45. 6

6a Spores borne on the surface of fruiting growths.

Order EXOSPORALES

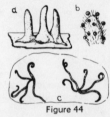

Fig. 44. *Ceratiomyxa fruticulosa.*
This is apparently the only known species of this order. It grows on rotten wood and is widely distributed. The fruiting bodies are white, sometimes tinged with pink or yellow.

Figure 44

6b Spores enclosed in fruiting bodies (sporangia). Various shades of brown, red, yellow and white.   Order ENDOSPORALES

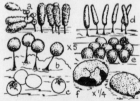

Fig. 45. a, *Arcyria ferruginea;*
b, *Lamproderma violaceum;*
c, *Physarum lateritium;*
d, *Comatricha pulchella;*
e, *Trichia persimilis;*
f, *Fuligo septica*

Figure 45

There are 285 species of slime molds known for North America. Many of these are easily found. They are most abundant from June to October.

7a Vegetative branches (mycelium) continuous (having no cross walls) (aseptate). Figs. 46 to 50. (The Algal-like Fungi). 8

Class PHYCOMYCETES

7b Mycelium with cross walls (septate). 12

29

KEY TO THE MORE COMMON ORDERS OF THE CLASS PHYCOMYCETES

8a Sexual reproduction by small spermatozoids and larger eggs, (heterogamous). Figs. 46 to 48. 9

Sub-Class, OOMYCETES

8b Sexual reproduction by fusion of equal sized motile sex cells, (isogamous). Figs. 49 and 50. 11

Sub-Class, ZYGOMYCETES

9a Conidia present. Parasitic on other plants.

Order PERONOSPORALES

Fig. 46. *Phytophthora infestans;* a, fungus growing from stoma of potato leaf; b, conidia producing zoospores; c, zoospore.

This is the causative agent of Late Blight of potatoes. It is highly destructive. It also attacks tomatoes. The order contains nearly 300 species, many of which are known as "downy mildews".

Figure 46

9b No conidia; reproducing only by sexual spores and zoospores. Figs. 47 and 48. 10

10a Plant filaments (mycelia) poorly developed; often only a single cell. Parasitic on other fungi, algae or seed bearing plants.

Order CHYTRIDIALES

Fig. 47. *Urophlyctis alfalfae.* a, Fruiting body within tissue of host; b, asexual spores; c, sexual spores; d, mature oospores within cell of host.

This parasite causes crown gall of alfalfa. The order includes some 280 species.

Figure 47

10b Mycelium well developed. Mostly aquatic molds. Large eggs fertilized by non-motile sperms which reach the egg through a tube. (The Water Molds). 　　　　　Order SAPROLEGNIALES

Fig. 48. *Saprolegnia;* a, growing on a dead insect in water; b, zoosporangia with zoospores; c, sexual reproduction.

This fungus is supposed to be a deadly enemy of fish. Some recent investigation seems to question that contention. The order includes more than 200 species representing some 25 genera.

Figure 48

11a Asexual spores several or numerous in sporangia. Mostly sapro-phytic. (The Black Molds). Order MUCORALES

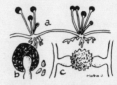

Figure 49

Fig. 49. Black bread-mold; *Rhizopus nigricans*, a, habit sketch; b, sporangium with spores; c, sexual reproduction with a zygospore. A very common household fungus.

A few of the some 400 species of this order cause plant or animal diseases, but most of them are saprophytic.

11b Asexual spores solitary in conidia. Parasitic on insects. Order ENTOMOPHTHORALES

Figure 50

Fig. 50. *Empusa;* a, a dead fly with mold; b, stages of sexual reproduction; c, filaments with conidiospores. The order includes some 60 species, all of which live as parasites or saprophytes on insects and likely aid materially in their control.

12a Spores borne in sacks (asci). Figs. 51 to 60. 13

Class ASCOMYCETES

12b Spores borne on clubs (basidia). Figs. 61 to 69. 21

Class BASIDIOMYCETES

KEY TO THE MORE IMPORTANT ORDERS OF ASCOMYCETES

13a Asci associated in groups, usually forming a hymenium. 14
Figs. 52 to 60. Sub-Class EUASCOMYCETES

13b Asci separate or scattered. Sub-Class PROTOASCOMYCETAE
This sub-class has but one order. (The Yeasts).

Order SACCHAROMYCETALES

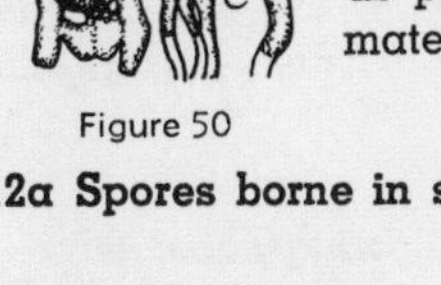

Figure 51

Fig. 51. *Saccharomyces cerivissae;* a, single plant; b, chain with buds; c, ascospores.

The yeasts, of which there are many species, resemble the bacteria in appearance but differ from them in cell structure, and average much larger, though the smallests yeasts are as tiny as the bacteria. The usual method of multiplication is by putting out buds at the side of the cell. These buds grow larger and break away.

All true yeasts produce spores in sacs which wins them a place among the Ascomytes. Yeasts are of high economic importance. The members of the Endomycetacea, belonging here, have mycelia and are parasitic on seed bearing plants.

31

SAC FUNGI

14a Asci not in a definite hymenium or receptacle.

Order EXOASCALES

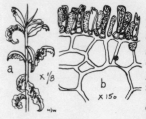

Fig. 52. a, Peach leaf with "Curl", *Exoascus deformans;* b, section through diseased leaf showing exposed asci and fungus threads. This disease is altogether too common on peaches, though not particularly destructive. Witches' brooms very common on hackberry and less frequent on several other plants, is caused by an organism from this group.

Figure 52

14b Asci in a definite receptacle, (ascocarp). Figs. 53 to 60. 15

15a Asci borne in a flattened, concave or closed sporocarp, often bordered by a distinct layer. Figs. 53 to 55. 16

15b Asci enclosed in a cylindric or spherical perithecium. Figs. 56 to 60. 17

16a Ascocarp subterranean; at maturity closed or tuber-like. (The Truffles).

Order TUBERALES

Fig. 53. *Tuber brumale;* a, fruiting body as dug; b and c, sections showing contents.

This and other species of truffles are edible. They are dug from the ground after being located by dogs or pigs trained for that purpose.

Figure 53

16b Apothecia, open from the start; head convex, pitted or gyrose (twisted).

Order HELVELLALES

Fig. 54. "Sponge Mushroom" - *Morchella.*

This is the so-called "edible Morel" and is the only "mushroom" collected and eaten by many persons, since anybody may be certain of its identity. They are common in damp woods in the spring.

Figure 54

16c Fruiting bodies disk-like or cup-like; at first closed but opening early.

Order PEZIZALES

Fig. 55. Black Goblet, *Geopyxis raterium.*
This species is readily recognized by its shape and black color. The fruiting bodies grow from 1 to 2 inches high. Many species have no stem. The order contains nearly 5000 species.

Figure 55

17a Perithecia borne on a short stem; microscopic fungi growing on insects. (Not at all common). **Order LABOULBENIALES**

Fig. 56. *Stigmatomyces;* a, entire plant; b, fruiting body with asci.
This species is known to occur on house flies. The order includes some 1200 species.

Figure 56

17b Perithecium sessile, solitary and free or united and embedded in a fleshy body. Figs. 57 to 60. 18
(Some orders in this group depend largely on conidiospores for their reproduction and the perithecia are rare.)

18a Asci when present (usually wanting) scattered through the perithecium. Saprophytic blue, green, black or yellow molds.
Order ASPERGILLIALES

Fig. 57. a, A fruiting head of *Aspergillus;* b-c, Fruiting head and habit sketch of *Penicillium;* d, Ascus with ascospores.
These molds are important in the home because of the food materials they "spoil". On the other hand they are valuable aids in the manufacture of cheese. The drug Pennicillin comes from *Penicillium notatum.*

Figure 57

18b Asci on a common level in the perithecium. Largely parasitic on plants. Figs. 58 to 60. 19

19a Mycelia usually growing parasitically on the surface of higher plants; perithecia scattered over surface of host; globose with no apparent ostiole; or flattened, with an ostiole. (The Mildews).
Order ERYSIPHALES

Fig. 58. Lilac mildew, *Microsphaera alni;* a, leaf of lilac showing growth of mildew; b, perithecium greatly enlarged showing asci. By mid-summer or later lilac leaves are very frequently covered with this pale gray parasite. Other related species are common on clover, willows, gooseberries and many other plants.

Figure 58

SAC FUNGI

19b Mycelium not highly superficial. Perithecia with ostiole.
Figs. 59 and 60. 20

20a Perithecia fleshy or membranous and colored. Frequently producing many conidiospores. (The Black Fungi).
Order HYPOCREALES

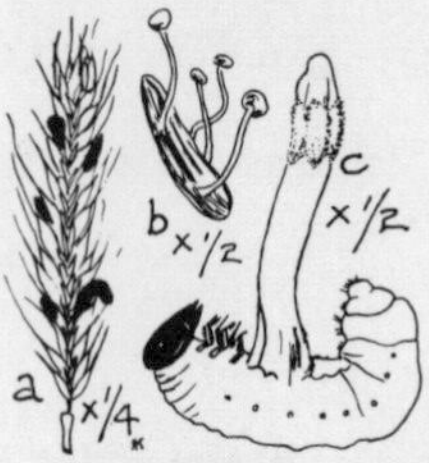

Fig. 59. Ergot; a, *Claviceps purpurea* on a head of rye; b, Sclerotium fruiting in the spring; c, *Cordiceps*, growing from a white grub.
Many insects attack plants; it is interesting as in *Cordiceps* to find the tables turned where a plant attacks and kills an insect.

Figure 59

20b Perithecia hardened, dark colored with distinct wall.
Order SPHAERIALES

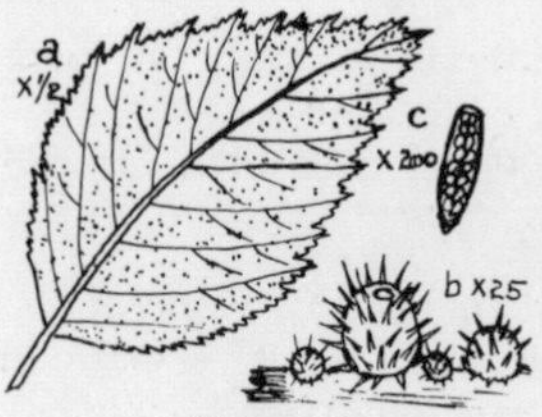

Fig. 60. *Coleroa chaetomium;* a, leaf of host with fruit spots (perithecia); b, perithecia; c, Ascus with eight double ascospores.
Many parasitic forms are found among the more than 10,000 species of this order.

Figure 60

KEY TO THE MORE COMMON ORDERS OF THE BASIDIOMYCETES

21a Great masses of usually black spores (chlamydospores) produced on the host plant, often on the floral parts, especially the ovaries of the grasses. Vegetative mycelia usually confined to interior of host tissue. (The Smuts).
Order USTILAGINALES

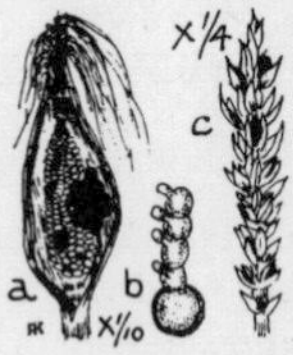

Fig. 61. Ear of corn with smut nodules, *Ustilago zeae;* b, promycelium (basidium) from germinating spore with sprout cells; c, head of wheat with smutted grains, *Tilletia tritici.*

Smuts are highly injurious to cereals and other crops. The farmer directly, and all of us incidentally, pay heavy toll to them. The number of spores produced is almost unbelievable. One heavily smutted ear of corn contains enough chlamydospores to furnish a few spores to each one of all the stalks of corn raised in the State of Iowa, "where the tall corn grows", in a single year. Little wonder that corn smut is so common.

Figure 61

21b Plants not as in 21a. Figs. 62 to 69. 22

CLUB FUNGI

22a Basidia septate. Mostly small parasitic plants, fruiting in reddish or brown rusty patches on host plant. A few gelatinous saprophytes. Figs. 62 and 63. ....**23**

22b Basidia not septate. Fruiting body usually conspicuous. Figs. 64 and 69. ....**24**

23a Parasites on other plants; often having alternating hosts and producing three or more types of spores. (The Rust Fungi).

Order **UREDINALES**

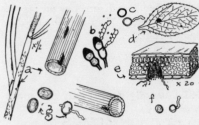

Figure 62

Fig. 62. Wheat Stem Rust, *Puccinia graminis;* a, Wheat stems with rust pustules; b, teliospores, black spores of fall and winter; c, basidiospores germinating in the spring; d, leaf of common barberry with aecia; e, cross section of barberry leaf showing an aecium; f, aeciospores, germinating; g, urediniospores, red spores of spring and early summer growing on wheat and other grass stems.

23b Saprophytes; with gelatinous fruiting body. (The Trembling Fungi and the Ear Fungi).

Order **TREMELLALES**

Figure 63

Fig. 63. a, *Auricularia;* b, *Tremella.*
Some systematists make two orders of these 200 species, putting the "Ear Fungi" in an order Auriculariales.

24a Spores arising from basidia which form a distinct membranous hymenium; hymenium is naked at maturity, and frequently covers the surface of gills, pores or spines. Figs. 64 to 66. ....**25**

24b Spores arising from basidia enclosed within the fruiting body. Figs. 67 to 69. ....**27**

25a Hymenium folded, toothed, covering gills or lining pores.

Figure 64

Order **HYMENOMYCETALES (In part)***
Fig. 64. a, *Aminita;* b, *Pholiota;* c, *Boletes;* d, *Hydnum;* e, *Polyporus.*
This group includes many edible mushrooms and a few exceedingly poisonous ones. If one should wish to die a most violent death, the eating of promiscuously picked mushrooms would offer a good chance to realize on his desire. The order also includes many woody forms with no food value.

CLUB FUNGI

25b Hymenium smooth. Figs. 65 and 66. 26
26a Fruiting bodies, usually small, leathery or membranous; smooth, warty or wrinkled. Mostly saprophytes.
Order HYMENOMYCETALES (In part)*

Fig. 65. a, *Stereum frustulosum;* b, *Stereum hirsutum.* These simple fungi are often found growing on pieces of oak and other dead woods. They sometimes display delicate shades of coloring.

Figure 65

26b Fruiting bodies clavate or coral-like, usually fleshy; only the upper portion spore bearing. (The Coral Fungi).
Order HYMENOMYCETALES (In part)*

Fig. 66. *Clavaria.*
The delicate shades, — yellow, white, pink, violet, together with the intricate branching, make the coral fungi unusually beautiful. Many of the species are edible.

Figure 66

27a Fruiting body at first, a fleshy egg-like structure with soft double walled outer membrane. At maturity the rapidly elongating hollow stalk bursts through the membrane and carries upward the chambered spore bearing head. Emits odor of carrion to attract the flesh flies. (The Stinkhorn Fungi).
Order GASTEROMYCETALES (In part)*

Fig. 67. *Ithyphallus impudicans,* a, mature fruiting body; b, c, d, different stages of younger fruiting body, breaking from enclosing volva.
These fungi never cease to attract attention. When immature they are often thought to be a nest of eggs. Rotting wood seems to offer the best habitat for their growth.

Figure 67

27b Not as in 27a. Figs. 68 and 69. 28

---

*These groups which formerly were listed as orders have more recently been given family significance.

28a Soft rounded fruiting bodies; fleshy when young, at maturity filled with masses of dust-like spores. (The Puff Balls).

Order GASTEROMYCETALES (In part)**

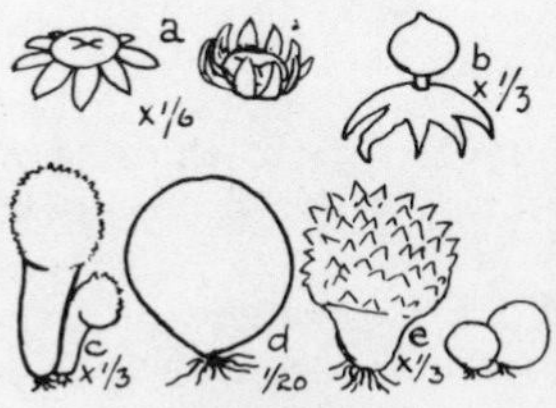

Fig. 68. a, Water measuring Earth-star, *Geaster hygrometricus*; b, Smallest Earth-star, *Geaster minimus*; c, Puff-ball, *Lycoperdon*; d, Giant Puff-ball, *Calvatia gigantea*; e, *Calvatia sculpta*.

No poisonous puff-balls are known. They make an abundant meal for one who enjoys mushrooms.

Figure 68

28b Fruiting bodies at maturity cup-like each containing several spherical egg-like bodies filled with spores. (The Birds-nest Fungi).

Order GASTEROMYCETALES (In part)**

Fig. 69. *Crucibulum*.

These interesting fungi are small and dull brown in color. The "eggs" are eventually blown out of the cup to scatter the spores.

Figure 69

KEY TO THE ORDERS OF THE
PHYLUM BRYOPHYTA (Mosses and Liverworts)

1a Plants growing flat without stem or leaves. Usually dark green.***
Figs. 70a and 72 to 75. (The Liverworts) 3

Class (in part) HEPATICAE

b Fig. 70. a, thalloid liverwort;
b, leafy liverwort.

Figure 70

1b Plants with a true stem or seeming to have a stem; erect, ascending, prostrate or hanging from trees. Figs. 70b and 71. 2

**These groups which formerly listed as orders are now reduced to family rank.

***Many Lichens (see Fig. 12) are flat growing and could be mistaken for liverworts. They are, however, gray, brown or yellow-green, especially when dry.

LIVERWORTS

2a Leaves with no mid rib, usually dark green, arranged in two opposite rows. These leaves may be rounded, lobed or cleft but usually have a part that folds under. (b-f)　　　Class HEPATICAE
　　　　　　　　　　　　　　　　　　Order JUNGERMANNIALES

Fig. 71. *Porella;* a, branch of plant showing reproducing bodies (sporophytes) (s); b, lower side
showing fold on leaf.
This is the largest of the five orders of Liverworts. Conard describes more than 80 species.

Figure 71

2b Leaves most often with mid rib; usually arranged equally around
the stem; sometimes flattened on two opposite sides, never lobed
or cleft and when rounded, not curved under at tips. From light to
dark green. Figs. 76 to 78. (The Mosses). 5
　　　　　　　　　　　　　　　　　　　　　　　　Class MUSCI

3a Sporophyte consisting of only a simple capsule embedded in the
tissue of the leaf-like plant. (No elaters.) Growing on mud flats or
floating on water.　　　　　　Order MARCHANTIALES (in part)

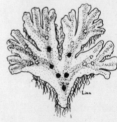

Fig. 72. *Riccia;* thallus showing rhizoids and reproductive bodies.
Some 20 species of this genus are known for
our country. *Ricciocarpus,* a genus similar in
appearance and habits also belongs here. Some
of these species float on water, while others
grow on damp soil.

Figure 72

3b Sporophyte not concealed on tissue of plant as in 3a.
Figs. 73 - 75. 4
4a Sporophyte with a stalk and a capsule of about equal length.
(Elaters present).　　　　　　　　Order MARCHANTIALES (in part)

Fig. 73. *Marchantia;* a, with cupules; b, with
archegoniophores, (female reproductive bodies); c, with antheridiophores, (male reproductive bodies); d, *Lunularia* with cupules, (asexual reproductive bodies).
The "gemma cups", each bearing several
little asexual gemmae which grow into new
plants vegetatively are very interesting.
These cups on *Lunularia* are half-moon
shaped.

Figure 73

38

4b Sporophyte with a stalk three or more times the length of the capsule. (Elaters present).　　　　　　Order METZGERIALES

Figure 74

x²/₃

Fig. 74. *Pellia*, with two sporophytes.

Conard describes six families and 13 common species of this order.

4c Sporophyte a slender horn-like capsule with no stalk, arising from upper surface of the plant. Capsule with center sterile piece (columella) but no elaters. (The Horn Liverworts).

Order ANTHEROCEROTALES

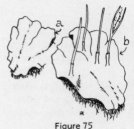

Figure 75

Fig. 75. Horned Liverwort, *Anthoceros*; a, vegetative thallus; b, thallus with sporophytes and spores.

Two species are known — *A. laevis* which is scattered entirely across our country and *A. fusimormis* with black instead of yellow spores which is known only from the Pacific Northwest.

5a Plants usually growing in bogs or very wet places; stems erect, much branched. Leaves usually light green or tinged with red, highly absorbent of water; with no mid rib. (Peat Moss, Sphagnum).

Order SPHAGNALES

Figure 76

Fig. 76. a, *Sphagnum squarrosum;* b, *Sphagnum acutifolium;* c, sporophyte (fruiting body) enlarged.

The order contains but a single genus but it has many species. Peat formed at the bottom of bogs by these plants is extensively used for fuel. The sponge-like water-holding qualities of the dead plants make is valuable for packing living plants. It has also been used extensively for surgical dressings.

5b Plants growing on rocks, usually in mountainous regions. Capsule very small, splitting along four lines. Leaves very small and almost black. (The Black Mosses). **Order ANDREALES**

Fig. 77. *Andreaea petrophila.*

Only five species of these tiny mosses are known in the United States. They are limited in height to a half inch. They are more abundant in our eastern mountains than those of the West.

Figure 77

5c Plants widely distributed in habitat; on rocks, trees, on wet or dry ground, in water, etc. (The True Mosses). **Order BRYALES**

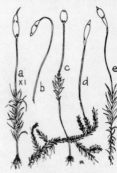

Fig. 78. a, *Tortella tortuosa;*
b, *Bryum caespiticium;*
c, *Schistostega osmundacea;*
d, *Leskea polycarpa;*
e, *Meesea triquetra.*

The true mosses have but little use commercially, but are so wide spread and so useful as to take high rank among our most valuable living things. Their role of soil holding and building alone, makes them exceedingly important. Aesthetically they lend much beauty to the landscape. There are many species; their collection and study is fascinating.

Figure 78

KEY TO THE ORDERS OF THE PHYLUM PTERIDOPHYTA (Ferns)

1a Delicate, often cut-leafed "fern-like" plants. Spores produced in sporangia usually born on the back of the leaves but in some species on special spore bearing parts. (The True Ferns).

Order FILICALES

Fig. 79. (This order of the Pteridophyta contains so many diverse forms that a number of species are shown).

a, Adder's Tongue, *Ophioglossum vulgatum;* b, Virginia Grape Fern, *Botrychium virginianum;* c, Walking Fern, *Camptosorus rhizophyllus;* d, Pepperwort, *Marsilea quadrifolia,* an aquatic species; e, Bulbet Fern, *Cystopteris bulbifera.*

Figure 79

1b Rush-like plants with jointed hollow stems, sometimes branched. Spores borne in cones at top of stem. (The Horsetails).

Order EQUISETINALES

Fig. 80. Field Horsetail, *Equisetum arvense;* a, whitish fertile stalk; b, green vegetative plant; c, Scouring Rush, *Equisetum hyemale.*

These interesting plants have hollow, jointed stems. They are often known as "Snake grass". The tissues are filled with silica. Bundles of these plants were commonly seen in the kitchens of the pioneers where they served as forerunners of the present "chore-boys".

Figure 80

1c Stems thickly clothed with small moss-like leaves. Spores produced in sporangia which are borne in the axils of scale-like or tubular leaves.

Order LYCOPODIALES

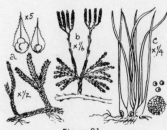

Fig. 81. a, Little Clubmoss, *Selaginella,* with megasporophyll and microsporophyll enlarged; b, Clubmoss, *Lycopodium;* c, Quillwort, *Isoetes,* with spores enlarged.

Clubmosses grow abundantly in the pine woods of our North and are often called "ground pine". The Little Clubmosses are sometimes raised as potplants and are spoken of as "table ferns". Quillworts grow in wet places.

Figure 81

KEY TO THE MORE IMPORTANT ORDERS OF THE PHYLUM SPERMATOPHYTA (Seed-Bearing Plants)

1a Ovules not enclosed in an ovary. Figs. 82 to 84. 2

Class GYMNOSPERMAE

1b Ovules enclosed in an ovary. Figs. 85 to 139. 4

Class ANGIOSPERMAE

2a Plants with column-like or tuberous stem crowned with leathery pinnately-compound leaves. Pollen grain and ovules borne each in their own cones. (In genus Cycas the ovules are borne on the edge of leaf-like structures). (The Cycads). Order CYCADALES

Fig. 82. *Cycas;* a, mature plant; b, staminate cone; c, carpellate cone.

The cycads are palm-like in general appearance. They are frequently raised as great pot plants in the North and as outdoor ornamentals in the South.

Figure 82

41

2b Not as in 2a. 3
3a Tree with leaves and fruit as pictured.   **Order GINKGOALES**

Figure 83

Fig. 83. Maiden-hair tree, *Ginkgo biloba*; a, staminate cones; b, young ovules; c, mature fleshy one-seeded fruit.

This interesting and rather beautiful tree is the sole living representative of what was likely a large order 100,000,000 years ago. It is a native of western China but is a fairly common ornamental tree with us.

3b Woody plants from shrubs to our largest trees. Leaves needle-like or scale-like. Pollen sacs borne in small cones. Seeds usually in larger cones (a few with single seed in fleshy covering).

Order CONIFERALES

Figure 84

Fig. 84. a, Red Cedar, *Juniperus virginiana*; b, Norway Spruce, *Picea abies*; c, Scotch Pine, *Pinus sylvestris*; d, Arborvitae, *Thuja occidentalis*; e, Canadian Hemlock, *Tsuga canadensis*.

This order while comparatively small includes many of our most valuable lumber trees. Most of them are evergreen.

4a Leaves usually parallel-veined (a); flowering parts usually in 3's (b); stems with bundles scattered throughout or hollow; seeds with one cotyledon. Figs. 85 and 89 to 99. (The Monocotyledons). 5

Figure 85

4b Leaves usually net veined (a); flowering parts usually in 5's (sometimes 4's) (b); stems with bundles arranged in ring around the pith, or woody with outer bark; seeds with two cotyledons. Figs. 86 and 102 to 138. (The Dicotyledons). 15

Figure 86

5a Carpels one or more distinct (rarely partly united); parts of the flowers mostly unequal in number. Figs. 87 and 89 to 95. 6

Figure 87

5b Carpels united to form a compound ovary; flowers usually complete, their parts mostly in 3's or 6's. Figs. 88 and 96 to 99. 12

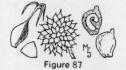

Figure 88

MONOCOTYLEDONS

6a Inflorescence of various forms but never a true spadix. Figs. 90 to 99. 7

6b Inflorescence a fleshy spadix with or without a spathe; or minute free floating plants with only occasional tiny flowers on leaf margin.   **Order ARALES**

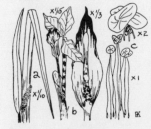

Fig. 89. a, Sweet Flag, *Acorus calamus;* b, Jack-in-the-Pulpit, *Arisaema triphyllum;* c, Duckweed, *Lemna.*

The corm or "bulb" of *Arisaema* is known as Indian turnip. Eaten raw it tastes like a red–hot poker.

Figure 89

7a Plants with palm type of foliage; leaves palmate or pinnate; large and stiff. (The Palms).   **Order PALMALES**

Fig. 90. a, Date palm, *Phoenix* sp.; b, Palmyra palm, *Borassus flabelliformis;* c, Cocoanut palm, *Cocos nucifera.*

Some of the world's most important plants belong to this order.

This large order is largely confined to the tropics. Its over 1200 members include great and small trees, shrubs and climbers. All are woody. The flowers are small and usually greenish.

Figure 90

7b Plants not as in 7a. Figs. 91 to 99. 8

8a Flowers surrounded by dry chaffy scales; (glumes) grouped into spikes or spikelets. (The Grasses and Sedges).

Order GRAMINALES

Fig. 91. a, Green Foxtail, *Setaria viridis;* b, Low Speargrass, *Poa annua;* c, Yellow Cyperus (a sedge), *Cyperus flavescens.*

This is one of the most important orders of the entire plant kingdom. The grass family is a very large one and contains many of the world's most valuable food plants such as wheat, corn, rice, etc.

Figure 91

8b Flowers not as in 8a. 9

9a Stamens and pistils scattered on the stem. Flowers without perianth; in spikes or heads; wind pollinated.

Order PANDANALES

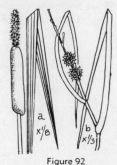

Fig. 92. a, Cat-tail, *Typha latifolium;* b, Burreed, *Sparganium.*

These are marsh plants and are widely distributed. One cat-tail head produces more than one million seeds.

Figure 92

9b Stamens and pistils placed in definite flowers. Figs. 93 to 99.... 10

10a Perianth, none or only rudimentary.

Order 2, NAJADALES (in part)

Fig. 93. Common Floating Pondweed, *Potomogeton natans.*

The members of this genus are submerged aquatic plants. The leaves often float. More than 60 species are known in our country. They play some very important parts in our lakes, ponds and streams.

Figure 93

10b Perianth present; with two sets of parts. 11

11a Carpels distinct.

Order NAJADALES (in part)

Fig. 94. Arrow-head, *Sagittaria.*

Many plants of this group have large arrow shaped leaves. They are often the most conspicuous plants along the water courses.

Figure 94

11b Carpels united in part. Aquatic plants.
Order NAJADALES (in part)

Fig. 95. Eel-grass, *Vallisneria*. (The flowers are enlarged).
It is often seen in home aquariums where is makes a superior aerating-plant. Its method of pollination makes an appealing study.

12a Flowers regular (a few with irregular petals). Figs. 96 and 97. 13

Figure 95

12b Flowers very irregular. Figs. 98 and 99. 14

13a Endosperm mealy; ovary superior.   Order XYRIDALES

Fig. 96. Spiderwort, *Tradascantia virginiana*.
The Wandering Jew and the Virginia Day-flower, both well known cultivated plants belong here. A native spiderwort with deep blue flowers is often abundant along railroad tracks.

Figure 96

13b Endosperm fleshy or horny. Ovary superior or inferior.
Order LILIALES

Fig. 97. a, Rush, *Juncus tenuis*; b, Poet's narcissus, *Narcissus poeticus*; c, Tulip, *Tulipa gesneriana*; d, Common Iris, *Iris germanica*.
Many of our most beautiful bulb plants belong to this large order. For delicacy, fragrance and universal interest they rank high.

Figure 97

14a Stamen (or stamens) not united with pistil to form a distinct organ.
Order SCITAMINALES

Fig. 98. a, Indian Shot, *Canna indica*; b, Banana. *Musa sapientum*.
Wind often seriously damages the foliage of plants. The members of this order have made provision for that hazard, by having leaves that may be readily slit transversely without lessening their value to the plant.

Figure 98

45

14b Stamen (or 2) grown together with the pistil to form a column; very irregular; ovary inferior. (The Orchids).

Order ORCHIDALES

Fig. 99. a, Lady's Slipper, *Cypripedium parviflorum;* b, Showy Orchid, *Orchis spectablis.*

This is another very large order. Its grandest species grow as epiphytes in the tropics. Our native orchids, — now all too rare, should be guarded carefully.

Figure 99

KEY TO THE ORDERS OF THE DICOTYLEDONS

15a Petals wholly separate from each other or wanting. Figs. 100 and 102 to 125. 16

Figure 100

15b Petals united, at least at their base. Figs. 101 and 126 to 139. 36

16a Petals none (except in the order Carophyllales including herbs with opposite leaves, rosemoss, purslane, pinks, chickweeds, etc.). Figs. 102 to 114. 17

Figure 101

16b Petals present. (Occasional species of several families have no petals). Figs. 115 to 125. 25

17a Calyx, none (except in some Juglandales). (Trees or Shrubs). Staminate flowers in aments. Figs. 102 to 105. 18

17b Calyx present. Figs. 106 to 114. 20

18a Leaves odd pinnate; fruit a nut enclosed in a husk. (The Walnuts and Hickories).

Order JUGLANDALES

Fig. 102. a, Hickory, *Carya ovata;* b, Black Walnut, *Juglands nigra.*

Some highly valuable woods and some of the most delicious nuts belong here. All members of the one family are trees.

Figure 102

18b Leaves simple (blade in one part). Figs. 103 to 105. 19

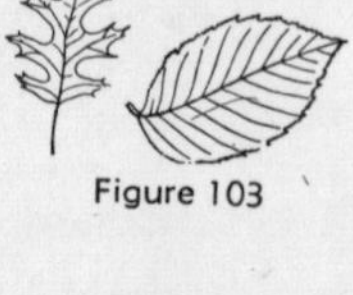

Figure 103

DICOTYLEDONS

19a Fruit one-seeded.　　　　　　　　　**Order MYRICALES**

Figure 104

Fig. 104. Bayberry, *Myrica carolinensis*.

The order contains but one family and only a few species. The bayberry is prized for its sweet-scented wax.

19b Fruit many seeded: seeds when ripe carried by wind by tuft of hairs at one end. (The Willows and Poplars).　Order SALICALES

Figure 105

Fig. 105. a, Cottonwood, *Populus deltoides*; b, Black Willow, *Salix nigra*.

The members of this order are trees. Their wood is light and of but little value for building, but is used for excelsior and packing crates.

20a Staminate flowers in aments, (tassel-like structures,-c). (The Birches and Oaks).　　　　　　　　　Order FAGALES

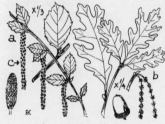

Figure 106

Fig. 106. a, River Birch, *Betula nigra*; b, White Oak, *Quercus alba*.

The oaks furnish very sturdy building timbers and make the most ideal furniture woods. There are many species of oaks.

20b Flowers not in aments. Figs. 107 to 114. 21

21a Ovary superior, flowers largely monoecious; one-celled.
　　　　　　　　　　　　　　　　　　　Order URTICALES

Figure 107

Fig. 107. a, Nettle, *Urtica gracilis*; b, White Elm, *Ulmus americana*; c, Hemp (Marijuana), *Cannabis sativa*.

Marijuana has come to be much in the public eye because of its narcotic properties.

DICOTYLEDONS

21b Ovary superior; flowers perfect. Figs. 108 and 112 to 114. ....**23**

Figure 108

21c Ovary inferior. Figs. 109 to 111. ....**22**

Figure 109

22a Ovary one-celled (a).   **Order SANTALALES**

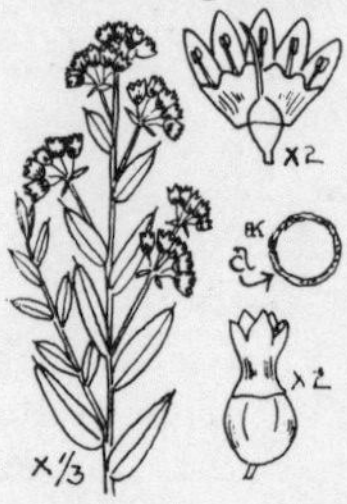

Fig. 110. Bastard Toad Flax, *Comandra umbellata.* This plant is often abundant in dry fields and on open woods hillsides. This small order includes but two small families.

Figure 110

22b Ovary several-celled (c) (usually 6); flowers perfect.
                                Order ARISTOLOCHIALES

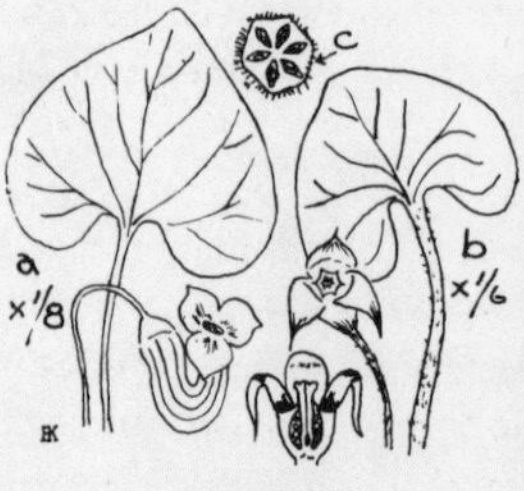

Fig. 111. a, Dutchman's Pipe, *Aristolochia macrophylla;* b, Wild Ginger, *Asarum canadense.*
The unusual shaped flowers enables one to recognize the members of this order at sight. Here again a small order includes only a few plants.

Figure 111

23a Fruit an achene (a dry one-seeded fruit,-c).
                                Order POLYGONALES

Fig. 112. a, Door-yard Knot-Grass, *Polygonium aviculare;* b, Smart Weed, *Persicaria persicaria.*
Several food plants and a large number of bad weeds fall in this order. It is an important group.

Figure 112

23b Fruit not an achene; embryo coiled, curved or ringed. Figs. 113 and 114. ....**24**

24a Fruit a one-celled capsule; petals usually present.
Order CARYOPHYLLALES

Fig. 113. a, Spring Beauty, *Claytonia virginica;* b, "Bouncing Betty", *Saponaria officinalis.*

The stems and leaves of *Saponaria* may be substituted for soap to clean one's hands. A common name is "Soapwort".

Figure 113

24b Fruit of various forms, not a one-celled capsule (no petals).
Order CHENOPODIALES

Fig. 114. a, Tumble Weed, *Amaranthus graeciozans;* b, Lamb's Quarters, *Chenopodium album.*

The order includes several very important families. Beets, Swiss Chard, and Spinach are among its food plants. Many highly annoying weeds likewise belong here.

Figure 114

25a Ovary arising above the calyx (superior) (some exceptions). Figs. 108 and 116 to 124. 26

25b Calyx growing from sides or top of ovary. Figs. 115 and 125 to 139. 34

26a Usually many single distinct carpels (occasionally carpels solitary or united). Stamens usually more numer- Figure 115 **ous than the sepals. (Many double forms in cultivation in which there may be no stamens, these organs having changed into petals.)**
Order RANUNCULALES

Fig. 116. a, Buttercup, *Ranunculus septentrionalis;* b, Water lily, *Castalia odorata;* c, Columbine, *Aquilegia canadensis.*

This large order includes a number of families of ornamental plants. The magnolias and the tulip tree are among its members.

Figure 116

26b Not as in 26a. Figs. 117 to 124. 27

27a Carpels two or more, united to form a compound ovary. Almost exclusively herbs. Sepals mostly distinct. Figs. 118 and 119. . .29

27b Not as in 27a. Figs. 117 and 120 to 124. .28

DICOTYLEDONS

28a Carpels solitary, or several and distinct, or united. Sepals usually united or confluent with a concave receptacle.

Order ROSALES

Figure 117

Fig. 117. a, Sweet-pea, *Lathyrus odoratus;* b, Alum root, *Heuchera hispida;* c, Iowa Crab, *Pyrus ioensis;* d, "Live-for-ever", *Sedum purpureum;* e, Mock Orange, *Philadelphus coronarius;* f, Wild Plum, *Prunus americana.*

This is a very large order containing some fifteen thousand species of widely diversified forms. There are two very large families; the Rose family with mostly regular flowers and the Pulse family in which the flowers are usually pea shaped.

28b Stamens arising at the base of or below the ovary. Carpels united into a compound ovary; sepals usually distinct. Figs. 120 to 124. 30

29a Plants trapping insects and securing some food material in this way. (Leaves basal). **Order SARRACENIALES**

Fig. 118. a, Pitcher Plant, *Sarracenia purpurea;* b, Sundew, *Drosera rotundifolia.*
We have several species of pitcher-plants, of which the Golden-trumpets *S. flava* is the grandest with graceful golden and red leaves up to 3 or 4 feet in height. The sundews are fragile little plants and disappointing when first seen. Look in bogs for these plants.

Figure 118

29b Plants not insectivorous as in 29a. Petals and sepals often 4. (Mustards, etc.) Some double forms (Poppies).

Order PAPAVERALES

Fig. 119. a, California poppy *Eschscholzia californica;* b, Dutchman's Breeches, *Dicentra cucullaria;* c, Shepherds' purse, *Bursa bursa-pastoris;* d, Typical mustard flower. The Mustard family, falling here is a highly important one. "Plants We Eat and Wear" describes 21 species of food plants included in it.

Figure 119

50

30a Stamens 10 or less. Figs. 120 to 122. ....,.....31

30b Stamens usually more than 10 (except in the violets and a few
others). Figs. 123 and 124. 33

31a Stamens as many as the sepals or fewer, and opposite them, or
more numerous. Figs. 121 and 122. 32

31b Stamens as many as the sepals and alternating with them.
Only woody plants; no herbs.   Order RHAMNALES

Fig. 120. a, Buckthorn, *Rhamnus lanceolata*;
b, Wild grape, *Vitis vulpina*.

At least four species of grapes are important for food.

Figure 120

32a Ovules usually pendulous; always turned away from the axis of
the ovary with the micropyle directed upward.
                                              Order GERANIALES

Fig. 121. a, Wild Crane's-bill, *Geran-
ium maculatum*; b, Yellow wood-sorrel,
Oxalis stricta; c, Flax, *Linum usitatis-
simum*; d, Wild Touch-me-not, *Impatiens
biflora*; e, Snow-on-the-mountain, *Euph-
orbia marginata*.

The Spurge family is the most important one in this large order.

Figure 121

32b Ovules pendulous but turned towards the axis of the ovary.
                                              Order SAPINDALES

Fig. 122. a, Poison Ivy, *Rhus toxico-
dendron*; b, Sugar Maple, *Acer sac-
charum*; c, Ohio buckeye, *Aesculus
glabra*.

Every lover of the out-of-doors should
know Poison Ivy for his own protection.

Figure 122

DICOTYLEDONS

33a Sepals meeting at their margins (valvate) in the bud. Stamens united in groups of five to ten (a); or all united in a column surrounding the pistil (b); (The Basswoods, Mallows, etc.)

Order MALVALES

Fig. 123. a, American Linden, *Tilla americana*; b, Low Mallow, *Malva rotundifolia*. Cotton and jute both come from plants in this order.

Figure 123

33b Sepals overlapping (imbricated) or rolled over each other (convolute) in the bud. (The Violets with irregular flowers and only 5 stamens belong here.)

Order VIOLALES

Fig. 124. a, Marsh Violet, *Viola cucullata*; b, St. John's Wort, *Hypericum ascyron*. Several families fall here, the Violet family having the most species.

Figure 124

34a Fleshy plants usually armed with spines and with joined stems. Sepals and petals for most part numerous, (Cacti).

Order OPUNTIALES

Fig. 125. Brittle Cactus, *Opuntia fragilis*. These plants are widely distributed, but are at their best in the deserts. Some species attain tree size.

Figure 125

34b Not as in 34a. Figs. 126 to 128. 35

35a Shrubs or trees; flowers without petals; only one ovule in ovary.

Order MYRTALES (in part)

Fig. 126. a, Leather wood, *Dirca palustris*; b, Russian Olive, *Elaeagnus angustifolia*.
The Russian Olive is a very hardy ornamental. Its silvery leaves and dense foliage make it a handsome plant. The long tough stems of Leather wood are used by the Indians to tie up bundles.

Figure 126

35b Petals present. Trees, shrubs or herbs, with opposite (or whorled) simple leaves. Ovules, several to many in each cavity of ovary.
Order MYRTALES

Fig. 127. a, Loosestrife, *Lythrum alatum;* b, Evening primrose, *Oenothera biennis.*
The Evening Primrose family is the large one in this order.

Figure 127

35c Petals present. Ovules one in each cavity of Ovary. Flowers borne in an umble.
Order UMBELLALES

Fig. 128. a, Wild Parsnip, *Pastinaca sativa;* b, Dogwood, *Cornus asperifolia.*
Fourteen food plants belong to the Parsley family included here.

Figure 128

36a Ovary growing above the calyx (superior). Figs. 108 and 129 to 136. 37

36b Ovary inferior. Figs. 109 and 137 to 139. 41

37a Stamens free from the corolla. Perennial shrubs and herbs with mostly evergreen leaves.
Order ERICALES

Fig. 129. a, Tall Blue-berry, *Vaccinium corymbosum;* b, Indian pipe, *Monotropa uniflora* (a white saprophytic plant).
Have you seen a nice bunch of Indian Pipe growing in woods or bog? You have missed a real thrill if you have not.

Figure 129

Figure 130

37b Stamens borne on the corolla, opposite its lobes (Fig. 130); or twice as many or more. 38

Figure 131

37c Stamens borne on the corolla, alternating with its lobes (Fig. 131); or fewer. 39

DICOTYLEDONS

38a Herbs (some woody forms in tropics). **Order PRIMULALES**

Fig. 132. a, Fringed Loosestrife, *Steironema ciliata;* b, Shooting-Star, *Dodecathon meadia.*

There is a sharp distinction between the real primroses belonging here and the Evening primroses.

Figure 132

38b Woody plants, — mostly tropical. **Order EBENALES**

Fig. 133. Persimon, Diospyros *virginiana.*
The green fruit is valuable as an aid in whistling. The tropical tree producing ebony wood belongs here.

Figure 133

39a Corolla thin, dry, without veins. (Herbs).

Order PLANTAGINALES

Fig. 134. Common Plantain, *Plantago major.*
Buckhorn, Bracted plantain and other serious weeds belong here. Our native species, *P. rugelii* is often more common than *P. major* which it closely resembles.

Figure 134

39b Not as in 39a. **40**

40a Two distinct ovaries; flowers regular, leaves usually opposite.
Order GENTIANALES

Fig. 135. a, Lilac, *Syringa vulgaris;* b, Swamp Milkweed, *Asclepias incarnata.* If you want to see something highly interesting, study the way the Milkweeds are pollinated.

Figure 135

40b One compound ovary (deeply four-lobed (e) in Boraginacea and Labiatae); flowers regular or irregular; stamens usually attached to corolla tube. **Order POLEMONIALES**

Fig. 136. a, Wild blue phlox, *Phlox divaricata;* b, Blue-bells, *Mertensia virginica;* c, Verbena, *Verbena officinalis;* d, *Salvia lanceaefolia;* e, *Salvia sclarea,* fruit; f, Beard's tongue, *Penstemon hirsuta;* g, Bittersweet, *Solanum dulcamara.*

Figure 136

41a Anthers united (a few exceptions). **Order CAMPANULALES**

Fig. 137. a, Pumpkin, *Cucurbita pepo;* b, Bell flower, *Campanula trachelium;* c, Cardinal Lobelia, *Lobelia cardinalis;* d, Goat's Beard, *Tragopogon pratensis;* e, Fleabane, *Erigeron* sp.

Figure 137

41b Anthers not united. **Order RUBIALES**

Fig. 138. a, Bed straw, *Galium aparine;* b, Bush Honeysuckle, *Lonicera tartarica;* c, Garden Heliotrope, *Valeriana officinalis.*
Many beautiful ornamentals are included in the Honeysuckle family belonging to this order.

Figure 138

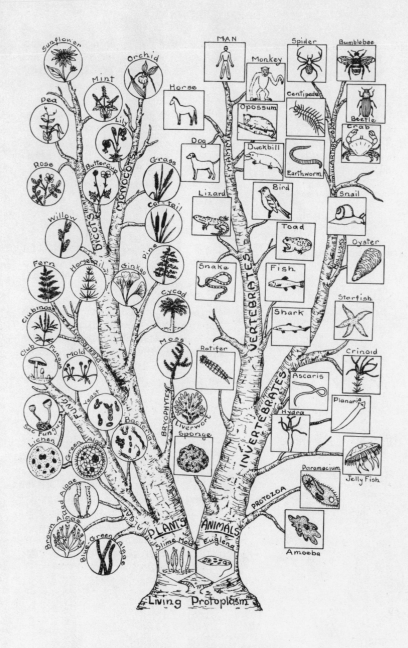

A Phylogenic Tree showing the approximate relationship of some common plants and animals.

KEY TO THE PHYLA OF THE ANIMAL KINGDOM

1a One celled animals, microscopic. (Many species multiply by cell division, and cling together in "colonies" which take the appearance of many celled animals. Such forms have no definite multicellular organs.) Figs. 139 and 146-171.

Phylum PROTOZOA p. 59

1b Animals composed of many cells and definite internal organs. (The Metazoa) .2

Figure 139

2a Body radially symmetrical, tube-like or without apparent symmetry. Figs. 140, 173, 177, 186, 229, etc. 3

Figure 140

2b Body bilaterally symmetrical. Figs. 141, 253, 270, 276, 407, etc. 6

Figure 141

3a Body with 2, 4, 6 or more, or without definite radii. Figs. 144, 175, 187, etc. 4

3b Body with five or an uneven number of radii. Aquatic animals covered with a "spiny skin". (The Star-fish, Sea Urchins, etc.) Figs. 225-239. Phylum ECHINODERMATA p. 84

4a Animals attached (except in early larval stage); no tentacles. Figs. 172-176. (The Sponges). Phylum PORIFERA p. 68

4b Free swimming animals. Figs. 185, 193, etc. 5

4c Unattached but non-swimming forms. Covered with spiny skin and having tube feet for locomotion. (The Star-fishes).

Phylum ECHINODERMATA (in part) p. 84

Figure 142

Fig. 142. *Leptasterias* sp.
Five or some multiple of five is the usual number of rays possessed by star-fishes. There are however, a number of exceptions, one of which is shown here to avoid confusion in the use of the key.

5a Outer surface with eight ciliated bands; two tentacles or none. (Marine.) 1 inch to 3 or 4 feet in size. Figs. 191-194. (The Sea Walnuts or Comb Jellies). Phylum CTENOPHORA p. 74

INVERTEBRATES

5b No cilia on outer surface, tentacles usually present, body wall
has stinging cells. Body often sac-like or umbrella-like. Aquatic.
(Mostly Marine). Figs. 177-190.   Phylum COELENTERATA p. 70

6a Respiratory organs internal, or related to paired gill slits in the
wall of the throat. Body supported by a spinal column (back-bone)
or in a few cases a notochord (a cartilagenous shaft).
Figs. 337-421.   Phylum CHORDATA p. 119

6b Respiratory organs not internal lungs or gills or in gill slits. (The
insects and spiders falling here, breath by internal trachea or
book lungs.) Figs. 244, 265, 317, 365, 390, etc. 7

7a Body with a calcareous (of lime) shell. Figs. 223, 247, etc. 8

7b Body without a calcareous shell. Figs. 143, 206, 252, 273, 371, 419,
etc. 9

8a Body covered with two shells; the larger one normally lying flat
and covered with the smaller; often attached to substratum by a
stalk. Marine. Figs. 223 and 224. (The Lamp Shells).
                                       Phylum BRACHIOPODA p. 83

8b Shell single, double or of eight plates. Both aquatic and land
forms. Figs. 240-250.   Phylum MOLLUSCA p. 88

9a Body externally segmented. Figs. 252, 259, 280, etc. 15

9b Body not externally segmented. Figs. 199, 212, etc. 10

10a Marine worms, burrowing in sand or mud; often forming tubes.
                                       Phylum PHORONIDEA

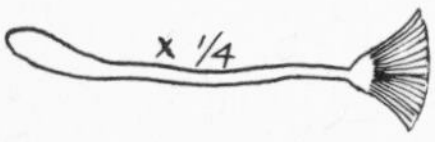

x ¼

Figure 143

Fig. 143. *Phoronis.*
Only a few species are known; all belong to
the same genus. They live often in colonies,
each animal in its own twisted chitinous tube.

10b Mostly non-burrowing. 11

11a Animals permanently attached, usually colonial. Figs. 220, etc.
                                       Phylum BRYOZOA p. 82

11b Animals unattached and usually free moving. Figs. 153, 250, 276,
385, etc. 12

12a Animals usually minute and aquatic (a few of the Chaetognatha
are not minute). Figs. 144, 145, etc. 14

12b Animals mostly not minute; often parasitic. Figs. 195, 206, 211,
etc. 13

13a Flattened worms. Figs. 195-208. **Phylum PLATYHELMINTHES p. 75**

13b Round thread-like worms. (The unsegmented Round Worms).
Figs. 209-213. **Phylum NEMATHELMINTHES p. 79**

13c Slimy elongated animals, with one or two pairs of tentacles at
anterior end. (The Slugs). Figs. 242e, 242f, and 243a.
Phylum MOLLUSCA p. 88

14a With one or more rings of cilia at the anterior end. Figs. 214-217.
(The Rotifers). **Phylum ROTIFERA p. 81**

Figure 144

Fig. 144. a, *Furcularia forficula*; b, *Philodina roseola*.
In the early days of the microscope these were called
wheel animalcules, because of the rings of cilia which
appear to rotate on the head. Most of the Rotifers are
solitary and free living. A few are marine but they are
much more abundant in fresh water. They may be easily reared in the laboratory and are often found in cultures of Protozoa.

14b **Without rings of cilia as in 14a. Marine. (The Arrow-worms).**
Phylum CHAETOGNATHA

Figure 145

Fig. 145. *Sagitta* sp.
The elongated slender transparent worms
belonging to this phylum are found
(often in great abundance) in all of the
seas. They seldom attain a length greater
than half an inch. About thirty species
are known.

15a With paired segmented appendages. Body usually with hard covering. Figs. 259-336. (The larvae of some insects have no legs.
See Figs. 323-325.) **Phylum ARTHROPODA p. 93**

15b Without segmented locomotory appendages. Usually fleshy and
worm-like. Figs. 251-258. (The segmented worms and leaches).
Phylum ANNELIDA p. 91

KEY TO THE CLASSES AND MORE IMPORTANT ORDERS OF THE PHYLUM PROTOZOA

1a Protozoa possessing cilia for locomotion and food getting.
Figs. 166-171. 3
Subphylum CILIOPHORA

1b Protozoa not possessing cilia. Figs. 147-165. 2
Subphylum PLASMODROMA

2a Moving by means of whip-like structures (flagella). Figs. 147-152.
Class MASTIGOPHORA p. 60

2b Moving by means of pseudopodia. Figs. 153-158.
Class SARCODINA p. 62

2c Parasitic; Locomotory organs usually wholly wanting. Figs. 159-165.   Class SPOROZOA p. 64

3a Cilia present during the entire life of the animal. Figs. 166-171.
Class CILIATA p. 66

3b Losing all cilia in mature stage. Adults attached and possess sucking tentacles. (One Order).   Class SUCTORIA

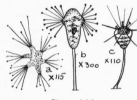

Figure 146

Fig. 146. a, *Trichophyra*; b, *Acineta*; c, *Podocyathus*.

This class together with the class Ciliata was formerly included in one class, the Infusoria. The Suctorians take many forms. They feed on other protozoans which they catch with their sucking tentacles. They also have sharp pointed tentacles for piercing.

KEY TO THE ORDERS OF THE CLASS MASTIGOPHORA

1a Usually possessing chromatophores (colored bodies). (Several common flagellates which do not contain colored bodies belong here since they are much like the other members of the subclass in spite of the color deficiency.) Figs. 147 and 148. 2
Subclass, PHYTOMASTIGINA

1b Without chromatophores (colored bodies containing chlorophyll). Figs. 149-152. 6
Subclass, ZOOMASTIGINA

2a Outer covering with a distinct transverse furrow and usually composed of plates; two flagella, one of which is transverse (in the furrow).   Order DINOFLAGELLIDA

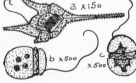

Figure 147

Fig. 147. a, *Ceratium*; b, *Glenodinium*; c, *Hemidinium*.

Only a limited number of species live in fresh water, most of the order being marine forms. They are sometimes claimed by the botanists who put them in the Dianophyceae.

2b Covering not composed of plates; without transverse furrow and flagellum. Figs. 17, 26 and 148. 3

3a Chromatophores green. (Red cytoplasmic granules in a few species). Figs. 17 and 148. 5

3b Chromatophores, yellow or brown. Fig. 26. 4

4a Body flattened, sac-like gullet (mouth cavity) present; not holozoic.   Order CRYPTOMONADIDA
These living creatures are claimed also by the botanists.

4b Body not flattened; no gullet evident.　Order CHRYSOMONADIDA
The members of this order are disputed forms.　See Fig. 26, p.23

5a Gullet (mouth cavity) present; reserve food material in form of
paramylum.　　　　　　　　　　　　　　Order EUGLENIDA

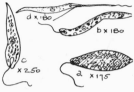

Fig. 148. a, *Euglena viridis*; b, *Euglena deses*;
c, *Astasia*; d, *Heteronema*.

This order contains a number of very common colorless genera some of which are saprozoic(e. g. *Astasia*) while others are holozoic (*Peranema, Heteronema*).

Figure 148

5b Without gullet.　　　　　　　　　　Order PHYTOMONADIDA
These forms are claimed by the botanists.　　See Fig. 17, p.20

6a With both pseudopodia and permanent flagella.
　　　　　　　　　　　　　　　　Order PANTOSTOMATIDA

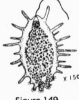

Fig. 149. *Mastigamoeba*.
Some species have several flagella. They are found in both fresh and salt water. Their usual type of reproduction is asexual.

Figure 149

6b Without pseudopodia, but with flagella. Figs. 150-152. 7

7a Flagella, one or two; mononucleate, free living (a-c), or parasitic
(d-e), especially in blood of vertebrates (Trypanosoma).
　　　　　　　　　　　　　　　　Order PROTOMONADIDA

Fig. 150. a, *Poteriodendron*; b, *Anthophysa*; c, *Bodo*; d, *Trypanosoma gambiense*, "Sleeping sickness" germ; e, *Cryptobia*.

This order includes parasitic, holozoic and saprozoic forms. Budding and longitudinal or multiple fission are the usual means of reproduction.

Figure 150

7b With one, two or several nuclei, and three to eight flagella per nucleus; free living or parasitic. Order POLYMASTIGIDA

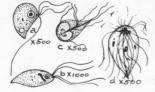

Figure 151

Fig. 151. a, *Tetramitis*; b, *Monocercomonas*; c, *Giardia*; d, *Coronympha*.
Most of this order inhabit the digestive tract of higher animals. The free living forms are both fresh water and marine.

7c Flagella more than eight; mononucleate. Parasitic in digestive tract of Xylophagous insects. Order HYPERMASTIGIDA

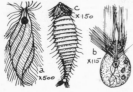

Figure 152

Fig. 152. a, *Holomastigotes*; b, *Staurojoenia*; c, *Cyclonympha*.
Many species of this order are found in the digestive tract of termites and are of especial interest in that they are thought to make the cellulose of the wood digestible for their host.

KEY TO THE MORE IMPORTANT ORDERS OF THE CLASS SARCODINA

1a Pseudopodia thin, straight and radiating with an axial filament in center (Axopodia). Figs. 157 and 158. 5
Subclass, ACTINOPODA

1b Pseudopodia broad and blunt projections containing both ectoplasm and endoplasm (Lobopodia); slender extensions of clear ectoplasm (Filopodia) or branching or anastomosing extensions. (Rhizopodia). Figs. 153-156. 2
Subclass, RHIZOPODA

2a Enclosed in a shell (test) with opening thru which pseudopodia project. Figs. 155 and 156. 4

2b Naked animals; not enclosed in shell. Figs. 153 and 154. 3

3a With more or less broad and blunt pseudopodia; both fresh water and marine, in soil and parasitic in animals.
Order AMOEBAEA

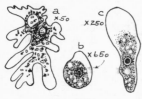

Figure 153

Fig. 153. a, *Amoeba*; b, *Entamoeba*; c, *Vahlkampfia*.
Almost everybody talks glibly about "amoebae", but there is still much to be discovered about these highly primitive animals. Just exactly how they put out their "false feet", for instance, seems unexplainable.

3b With radiating pseudopodia, sometimes branching or anastomosing. **Order PROTEOMYXA**

Figure 154

Fig. 154. a, b, *Pseudospora;* c, d, *Nuclearia.*

The members of this order are rather poorly understood. Many of them seen to live parasitically on green water plants.

3c Pseudopodia, branching and anastomosing; individuals fusing to form plasmodium, which later forms complex sporangia. See Figs. 39 and 43-45. **Order MYCETOZOA**
More plant-like than animal-like.
See Myxothallophyta, p. 29.

4a Shell with but one chamber, organic or composed of foreign bodies cemented together (arenaceous); fresh water.
Order TESTACEA

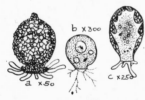

Figure 155

Fig. 155. a, *Difflugia;* b, *Lecythium;* c, *Nebela.*

The members of this order are rather readily recognized by the shell surrounding the living cell. Some live in moist acid soil; a very few marine forms are known.

4b Shell usually limy; some are silicaceous or arenaceous; of one to many chambers; marine. **Order FORAMINIFERA**

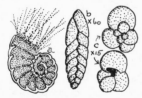

Figure 156

Fig. 156. a, *Peneroplis;* b, *Bolivina;* c, *Globigerina.*

Many fossil forms found in chalk deposits. They are useful in identifying geological strata in oil well drilling.

5a With central capsule; marine. Many species with elaborate skeletons of silicon or strontium sulphate.　　　Order RADIOLARIA

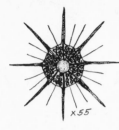

Fig. 157. *Acanthometron*.

The known species of this order runs into thousands. They take many forms and are partly enclosed in a shell or skeleton.

The skeletons have been so numerous as to form many of the geological strata.

Figure 157

5b Without central capsule; mostly fresh water.　　Order HELIOZOA

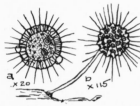

Fig. 158. a, *Actinosphaerium*; b, *Clathrulina*.

Some members of this order are attached, though most of them are free swimming. Some species possess a skeleton, others are naked. They inhabit fresh water for the most part.

Figure 158

KEY TO THE MORE IMPORTANT ORDERS OF THE CLASS SPOROZOA

1a Sporozoa in which spore formation ends the individual life of the organism; i. e., sporozoites develop from a zygote. Figs. 159 and 160. 3
Subclass, TELOSPORIDIA

1b Sporozoa with spore formation occurring during the vegetative stages. Figs. 162-165. 2

2a Spores with polar filaments coiled in capsule. Figs. 162 and 163. .4
Subclass, CNIDOSPORIDIA

2b Spores without polar filaments. Figs. 164 and 165. 5
Subclass, ACNIDOSPORIDIA

3a Very small intracellular parasites; asexual multiplication usually in digestive tract or liver of vertebrates or in higher invertebrates. Zygote non-motile. Sporozoites within spore capsule.

Order COCCIDIA

Figure 159

Fig. 159. *Eimeria.*
Our domestic animals and poultry are hosts to numerous species of this order.

3b Very small intracellular parasites; asexual multiplication in erythrocytes or endothelial cells of vertebrates; zygote motile and found in alimentary canal of blood sucking invertebrates. Sporozoites not within spore capsules. Order HAEMOSPORIDIA

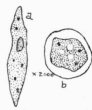

Figure 160

Fig. 160. Malaria fever germ, *Plasmodium vivax.*
(a) In mosquito;
(b) In blood corpuscle of man. Members of this order cause malaria in man and birds and Texas fever of cattle.

3c Large extracellular parasites of gut and body cavities of invertebrates, especially arthropods and annelids.

Order GREGARINIDA

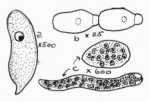

Figure 161

Fig. 161. a, *Monocystis;* b, *Gregarina;* c, *Schizocystis.*
Earth worms, mosquitos, flat worms, cockroaches, crickets, beetles, centipedes, mollusks, crabs, and flies are among the known hosts to the Gregorines. It would seem that this group would offer a fruitful field for discovery of new species.

4a Spore large with bivalved membrane; polar capsules visible in living state. Order MYXOSPORIDIA

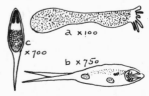

Figure 162

Fig. 162. a, *Myxidium;* b, *Agarella;* c, *Henneguya.*
The spore varies much in size and shape. The species of this order are largely parasitic on fish and amphibians.

4b Spore small with one piece membrane; polar capsules invisible in living state. Order MICROSPORIDIA

Figure 163

Fig. 163. Spores of a, and c, *Stempellia* (host mosquito); b, *Plistophora* (host black fly larva). The microsporidia for the most part live parasitically on fish and arthropods. Silk worms and honey bees each have a disease of which these protozoa are the causative agent.

5a Embedded in muscles of higher vertebrates.

Figure 164

Order SARCOSPORIDIA

Fig. 164. *Sarcocystis*.

The order has but this one genus. Ducks, rabbits, horses, mice, pigs, sheep and man are known hosts.

5b Parasites of invertebrates and fish. Order HAPLOSPORIDIA

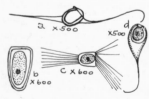

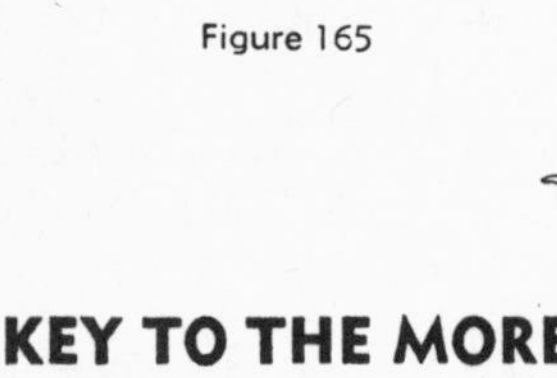

Figure 165

Fig. 165. a, b, c, Spores of different species of *Haplosporidium*; d, Spore of *Urosporidium*.

Rotifers, annelid worms, fish, cockroaches, etc., serve as hosts to these parasites.

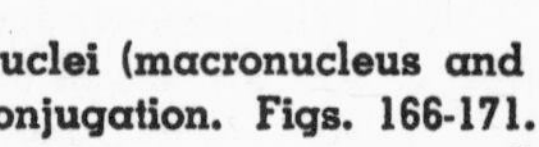

KEY TO THE MORE IMPORTANT ORDERS OF THE CLASS CILIATA

1a Having two sizes of nuclei (macronucleus and micronucleus). Sexual reproduction by conjugation. Figs. 166-171. 2
Subclass, EUCILIATA

1b With two to many nuclei, all of one type. Sexual reproduction by copulation. Subclass, PROTOCILIATA
But one order. Parasitic in intestine of amphibians or fish.

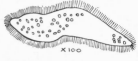
Figure 166

Fig. 166. *Cepedia;* parasitic in intestine of frog.
One needs only to examine the intestine of a few frogs or toads if he wishes to get specimens of this order.

2a With adoral zone (heavily ciliated groove leading to mouth). Figs. 168-171. 3
2b Without adoral zone; cilia present on all parts of the body.
Order HOLOTRICHIDA

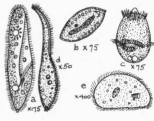
Figure 167

Fig. 167. a, *Paramecium caudatum;* b, *Hoplitophrya,* parasitic in intestine of earthworm; c, *Didinium;* d, *Lionatus;* e, *Chilodon.*
This is a large order. Its members may be found living a free life in both fresh and salt water while some are parasitic.

3a Cilia over the entire body. Adoral zone turns to left.
Order HETEROTRICHIDA

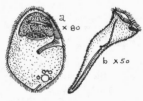
Figure 168

Fig. 168. a, *Nyctotherus;* b, *Stentor.*
The direction of the adoral zone is not a very good character since in semi-transparent animals it is difficult to be sure of directions. There are both parasitic and free living forms.

3b Cilia not over the entire body. Figs. 169-171. 4
4a Adoral zone surrounding mouth turning to left. Figs. 170 and 171..5
4b Adoral zone turning to right. Without cilia except on one or more rings surrounding body. Order PERITRICHIDA

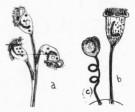
Figure 169

Fig. 169. a, *Epistylis;* b, *Vorticella.*
Both free swimming and stalked forms are found in this order. A few are parasitic. When the animal is disturbed the stock is quickly coiled (c) to withdraw the animal from danger.

5a Cilia few or wholly wanting except on adoral zone.
                                        Order OLIGOTRICHIDA

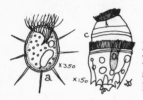

Fig. 170. a, *Halteria;* b, *Ophryoscolex.*
Most of the species belonging here are parasitic. Cattle, sheep and horses are frequently hosts.

Figure 170

5b Cilia on ventral side only, where they are fused in groups to form cirri.
                                        Order HYPOTRICHIDA

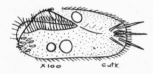

Fig. 171. *Stylonichia.*
These are largely free living forms in fresh or salt water. A few are parasitic. They are flattened in form with the cilia on the ventral side only.

Figure 171

KEY TO THE MORE IMPORTANT ORDERS OF THE PHYLUM PORIFERA (SPONGES)

1a Small marine sponges, mostly gray or white, with skeleton of limy spicules. Rarely over one inch long. Figs. 172 and 173. 2
                                        Class CALCAREA
1b Larger sponges; with fibers of spongin or spicules of silica or both. Rarely without either. Figs. 174-176. 3
                                        Class NONCALCAREA
2a Thin walled narrow tube-like sponges. Collar cells (a) in central cavity.
                                        Order HOMOCOELA

Fig. 172. *Leucosolenia.*
These simple little marine sponges are rather widely scattered in shallow water. They are usually white or yellowish.

Figure 172

2b Body wall thicker; collar cells within the pores.

Order HETEROCOELA

Figure 173

Fig. 173. *Grantia*.
There are many species of this and the related genera. Most of them are white or colorless.

3a Skeleton of horny fibers as known in common bath sponges. Spicules are absent but grains of sand and other minute foreign bodies are often imbedded and form a part of the skeleton.

Order KERATOSA

Figure 174

Fig. 174. Sheepswool sponge, *Hippospongia gossypina*.
Raising commercial sponges and fishing for them is a highly important activity. Few if any other animals can regenerate from such small fractional parts as sponges.

3b With 6-rayed spicules of silicon (with 3 axes). Tubular or cup shaped forms from deep sea. (Glass Sponges).

Order HEXACTINELLIDA

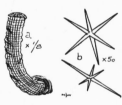

Figure 175

Fig. 175. a, *Euplectella;* b, triaxon spicules.
This is a small order. They are found at considerable depth in tropical seas. They have no commercial importance.

3c Spicules of silica always present but none of them six rayed (with 3 axes). May or may not have spongin fibres.

Order TETRAXONIDA

Figure 176

Fig. 176. A fresh water sponge, *Spongilla* covering a plant stem.
These are found in clear running water. They sometimes cover an area of one by two feet or more.

KEY TO THE MORE IMPORTANT ORDERS OF THE PHYLUM COELENTERATA

1a Corals, sea anemones, etc. Restricted to the polyp form; no medusae produced. Figs. 189 and 190. 11
Class ANTHOZOA

1b Large and small medusae and small hydroid polyp forms. Figs. 177-188. 2

2a Hydroids usually colonial; no mesentarial ridges. Medusae mostly minute; possessing a velum. Figs. 177-183. 3
Class HYDROZOA

2b Hydroid forms minute; with 4 mesentarial ridges; medusae usually larger than in 2a; no velum present. Figs. 184-188. 7
Class SCYPHOZOA

3a Fresh water forms. Elongate, cylindrical animals with tentacles surrounding mouth.
Order HYDRARIAE

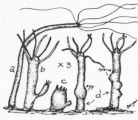

Fig. 177. *Hydra;* a, an animal fully extended; b, reproducing asexually by budding; c, same as b but contracted; d, reproducing sexually by eggs and sperms.

Most of the Coelenterates are marine but Hydra are fresh water species and are widely scattered. Living specimens are highly interesting and worth looking for.

Figure 177

3b Marine animals (a few exceptions). 4

4a Colonial forms attached to rocks and other objects and forming a coral-like base.
Order HYDROCORALLINAE

Fig. 178. *Distychophora coccinea;* a, Portion of colony showing branching; b, Edge view of branch showing large gastropores and small dactylopores. (Pacific Ocean).

These animals so closely resemble corals that for years the scientists thought they belonged there. It is then little wonder that the casual observer is often fooled.

Figure 178

4b Not coral-like. 5

5a Colony and hydroids, if present, minute. Medusae usually hemispherical or elongate. Order TRACHOMEDUSAE

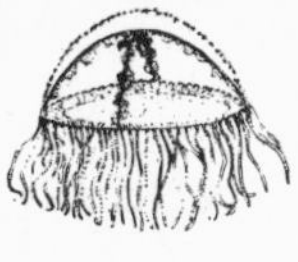

Fig. 179. *Gonionemus.* — widely distributed.

By freeing itself of a polyp stage which would need to live an attached life near the shore, the members of this order have been permitted to take to the open sea.

Figure 179

5b Colony free swimming, polymorphic (having several forms of polyps in the colony). Order SIPHONOPHORA

Fig. 180. "By-the-wind-sailor", *Velella lata;* a, entire colony; b, diagramatic cross section showing organization of colony.

The Portugese Man-of-war, abundant in the Gulf Stream is the best known of this order. The colony is characterized by its many different forms and very long tentacles, some being almost 50 feet in length.

Figure 180

5c Colony and individual hydroids not minute. With not more than two types of polyps. 6

6a Hydranth surrounded by a protecting cup (hydrotheca). Medusae when mature often disk-like; gonads on sub-umbrella and sometimes also on manubrium. Order CAMPANULARIAE

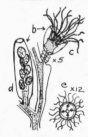

Fig. 181. *Obelia* sp.; a, Portion of colony showing (b) hydrotheca surrounding (c) hydranth and (d) gonangium; e, Medusa.

With plants, alternation of generations is the usual thing. Here are animals that strongly portray that phenomenon.

Figure 181

6b Hydranth without a protecting cup. Medusae with gonads on the manubrium alone. Order TUBULARIAE

Fig. 182. *Pennaria tiarella;* a, Portion of colony showing hydranth; b, Female medusa with c, gonads.

Many of these animals live in colonies of greatly branched tree-like form up to 6 inches in height. The order is a large one.

Figure 182

6c No hydranth known. Medusae with margin of umbrella scalloped.
                                      Order NARCOMEDUSAE

Figure 183

Fig. 183. *Cunoctantha.*

A small order of medusa forms, largely confined to the open ocean although a few are found along the coast.

7a No medusae. Hydranth attached by stalk.

Order STAUROMEDUSAE

Figure 184

Fig. 184. *Haliclystus* sp. Side view. Pacific Ocean.

These forms live in shallow water where they are usually attached to sea weed. Some 25 species are known.

7b Having free swimming medusae. 8

8a Medusae constricted at middle; margin usually with 16 lobes.
                                      Order CORONATAE

Figure 185

Fig. 185. *Pericolpa.*

As the name indicates the medusae are crown shaped. The margin usually has 16 lobes. They are usually found well out at sea. Some 30 species are recorded.

8b Medusae without constriction. Figs. 186-188. 9

9a Medusae with tentacles on margin or on subumbrella. Figs. 187 and 188. 10

9b Medusae having no tentacles on margin or on subumbrella; 8 oral lobes extending from center of subumbrella.

Order RHIZOSTOMAE

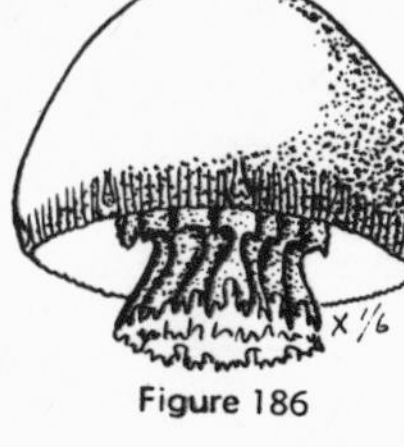

Fig. 186. *Stomolophus.* Common along our eastern Atlantic coast.

For the most part jelly fishes have no practical value; one species of this order is used for food in the Orient.

Figure 186

10a Medusae with 8 or more tentacles on margin or subumbrella.
Order SEMAEOSTOMEAE

Fig. 187. *Aurelia.*

Some of the jelly fish belonging here are nearly x/2 two feet in diameter and may have tentacles more than 100 feet in length. Add to this the brilliant colors some species possess, and we have some highly interesting animals.

Figure 187

10b Medusae somewhat cube shaped with 4 long tentacles.
Order CUBOMEDUSAE

Fig. 188. *Charybdaea.*

Again the name plainly indicates the character of the order. The medusae are somewhat flat-sided. The order contains less than 20 species. They are Atlantic coast forms.

Figure 188

11a With many simple tentacles, (Stony Corals and Sea Anemones.)
Order ZOANTHARIA

Fig. 189. a, *Epiactis prolifera*, Pacific Ocean; b, *Metridium dianthus*, common along our Atlantic coast, also in the Pacific Ocean.

The sea anemones are greatly admired for their interesting form and attractive colors. Many of them closely resemble flowers.

Figure 189

11b With 8 feather-like tentacles.
Order ALCYONARIA

Fig. 190. "Dead man's fingers", *Anthomastis rilleri.*

Here is found many of the most brilliantly colored Living Things of the ocean. In addition to their bright hues some are phosphorescent and highly conspicuous. The order includes more than 2000 species.

Figure 190

KEY TO THE CLASSES AND ORDERS OF THE PHYLUM CTENOPHORA

1a With either oral·lobes or tentacles. Figs. 192-194. 2
Class TENTACULATA

1b With neither oral lobes nor tentacles.
Class NUDA
Order BEROIDEA

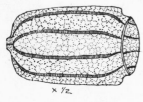

× ½

Figure 191

Fig. 191. *Beroe*. Very abundant and widely distributed. They are sometimes greatly distended by swallowing animals larger than themselves. The one family of this order contains some 15 species. They are sometimes 8 inches in length.

2a Body flattened and ribbon-like. Up to four feet in length.
Order CESTIDA

× 1/20

Figure 192

Fig. 192. "Venus' girdle", *Cestus veneris*, Tropical, transparent, with irridescent tints of blue, pink and green.

2b Body compact. Figs. 193 and 194. 3

3a With long tentacles.
Order CYDIPPIDA

× 1/3

Figure 193

Fig. 193. *Hormiphora*.

These are soft, partly transparent jelly fishes. Like other members of the phylum both sexes are represented in each individual. (Hermaphroditic).
The tentacles are used for food gathering. They are armed with stinging hairs.

3b With oral lobes but no tentacles.   Order LOBATA

Fig. 194. *Mnemiopsis*. Abundant along Atlantic coast. Transparent but highly phosphorescent at night.

The total number of Ctenophores will not run much over 100. Animals like these seldom have any economic importance.

Figure 194

KEY TO THE CLASSES AND THE MORE COMMON ORDERS OF THE PHYLUM PLATYHELMINTHES

1a No anus, no circulatory system, animals usually hermaphroditic. Fresh water, marine or parasitic. Figs. 196-208. 2

1b With anus, long evertable proboscis at anterior end for attachment and defense or offense, and a circulatory system. With a few exceptions, marine, unisexual and free living. Range in size from less than an inch to over 90 feet in length. Sometimes, under certain conditions, round in cross section. Often brilliantly colored.
                                              Class NEMERTINEA

Fig. 195. a, *Oerstedia*; b, *Tetrastemma*; c, *Cerebratulus*.
Some zooligists would make a separate phylum of this group. More than 500 species are known.

Figure 195

2a Elongate, free living flat worms. Body covered with cilia. Figs. 196-200. 4
                                              Class TURBELLARIA

2b Parasites on or within larger animals. No external cilia. Figs. 201-208. 3

3a With mouth (usually at forward end) and with intestine. Adults from microscopic to 4 inches in length; never segmented. Many species have two or more hosts and include a number of types of individuals while developing. Figs. 201-205. 7
                                  (The Flukes) Class TREMATODA

FLATWORMS

3b Mouth and intestine absent. Usually long and seemingly segmented. Internal parasites; almost always with two or more hosts of different species. Figs. 206-208. 10
(The Tapeworms) Class CESTOIDEA

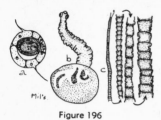

Figure 196

Fig. 196. "Beef Tapeworm", *Taenia saginata;* a, egg; b, cysticercus or bladder worm; c, mature worm.

The Tapeworms appear to be segmented which seems contradictory to the definition of the phylum. The segments, or proglottids, however are plainly independent units which are budded asexually from the scolex.

4a Tiny marine species with no intestine. Often brilliantly colored.
Order ACOELA

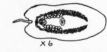

Figure 197

Fig. 197. *Polychaerus,* Atlantic coast.

These small free swimming forms are found among the rocks and seaweeds off shore. They feed on minute plants and animals.

4b With intestine. Figs. 198-200. 5

5a Intestine a single blind tube; unbranched. Size up to 3/5 of an inch in length; usually much smaller.   Order RHABDOCOELIDA

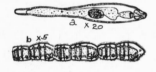

Figure 198

Fig. 198. a, *Stenostomum;* b, *Microstomum,* part of chain with 3 individuals.

These animals live on land or in both salt and fresh water. Asexual reproduction is common.

5b Intestine branched. Usually larger than in 5a. Figs. 199 and 200...6

6a Intestine three branched (one branch extending forward and two back from mouth near middle of body). Eyes, usually two. Fresh water, terrestrial and marine.   Order TRICLADIDA

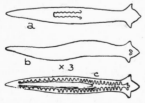

Figure 199

Fig. 199. *Planaria;* a, ventral view showing proboscis; b, dorsal view; c, showing 3-branched intestine.

There are some land forms which occur in very moist places. Planaria are unusually well adapted for experiments in regeneration. They are found under stones and among algae.

76

6b Intestine with more than three large branches. Eyes, usually numerous. (Wholly marine).   **Order POLYCLADIDA**

Fig. 200. *Planocera.*

They range up to one inch in length with more than half that width. Many species are highly translucent.

Figure 200

7a Externally parasitic on fish and other aquatic animals. (The family Polystomidae are internal parasites). Hooks for attachment usually present in suckers or disk. Figs. 202 and 203. 8
    Subclass, MONOGENEA

7b Usually internal parasites requiring two or more hosts. Without hooks in suckers. Figs. 201, 204 and 205. 9
    Subclass, DIGENEA

Fig. 201. Typical life history of a *Cotylophoron cotylophorum.*

Some dangerous parasites of man and the domestic animals fall here.

Many of the parasitic flat worms have a very complicated life cycle with several forms in one or more of their hosts. They multiply to amazing numbers.

Figure 201

8a Posterior end of adult with one large sucking disk (a) for attachment.   **Order MONOPISTHOCOTYLEA**

Fig. 202. *Anonchohaptor anomalum.*
Ventral view of a mounted specimen (after Mueller, 1938).

Some species attack the gills of fish. There are doubtless many species not now known.

Figure 202

8b Posterior attachment organ bearing two or more suckers (a).
    Order POLYOPISTHOCOTYLEA

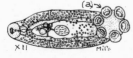

Fig. 203. *Polystoma orbiculare.* Ventral view of mounted specimen. (After Stunkard, 1917).

These too, attack the gills of fish and amphibians. They range in length up to one-sixth of an inch.

Figure 203

FLATWORMS

9a Mouth of adult near middle of body (a); (never in anterior sucker).
Order GASTEROSTOMATA

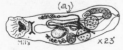

Figure 204

Fig. 204. *Bucephalus papillosus*. Ventral view. (After Woodhead, 1929).
The cercaria live in mollusks while the adults parasitize several species of fish.

9b Mouth of adult at anterior end of body and usually surrounded by oral sucker (a). Intestine usually two branched.
Order PROSOSTOMATA

Figure 205

Fig. 205. *Glypthelmins quieta*. Dorsal view of living worm. (After Miller, 1930).
This is a very large order of species known by one or more stages only. The full life history has not been worked out for most of them.

10a Adult forms parasitic in warm blooded veterbrates (both birds and mammals). Scolex with 4 cup-like suckers. Slender forms up to 40 feet in length.
Order CYCLOPHYLLIDEA

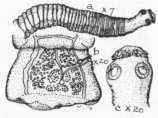

Figure 206

Fig. 206. *Taenia twitchelli;* a, anterior portion of strobila; b, mature proglottid; c, scolex. (After McIntosh, 1938).
These are rather common parasites of birds, mammals, and reptiles. The order is a large one.
Man becomes infested by eating raw or poorly cooked meat.

10b Parasitic almost always in fish or other cold blooded animals. Figs. 207 and 208. 11

11a Scolex with 4 suckers or bothria (projections or grooves on scolex of tape worms, functioning as suckers).
Order TETRAPHYLLIDEA

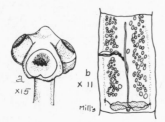

Figure 207

Fig. 207. *Crepidobothrium gerrardii;* a, scolex; b, mature proglottid. (After La Rue).
Some of these tapeworms attain a length of 10 to 15 inches. They live in the intestine of fish, amphibians, and reptiles.

78

11b Scolex with but two suckers or bothria.

Order PSEUDOPHYLLIDEA

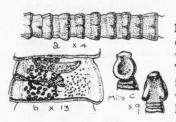

Figure 208

Fig. 208. *Abothrium crassum;* a, section of strobila; b, a ripe proglottid; c, two views of scolex. (After Cooper, 1918). This is a rather small order, parasiting fish, reptiles and birds. It seems that whether the host was a warm or cold-blooded animal would make considerable difference with a parasite.

KEY TO THE CLASSES AND MORE COMMON ORDERS OF THE PHYLUM NEMATHELMINTHES

1a With spiny proboscis at tip of forward end for attachment to intestinal wall of host. No mouth, intestine or anus.

Class ACANTHOCEPHALA
Order ECHINORHYNCHOIDEA

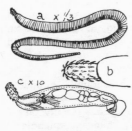

Figure 209

Fig. 209. a, Spine headed worm, *Echinorhynchus gigas;* b, proboscis showing spines; c, *Acanthocephalus ranae,* an amphibian parasite.

One species of spine headed worm is a frequent parasite of hogs. Since the May beetle and its larvae, the white grub is the alternating host of these worms, pigs must be kept from feeding on these insects, although that offers one excellent way to control the grubs. There are some schemes by which one can get around the difficulty.

1b Without spiny proboscis as in 1a. Intestine present. Figs. 210-213. 2

2a Round worms usually white or flesh colored; tapering at posterior end; two lateral lines (elongated streaks or ridges) present. Intestinal parasites and free living in ground. 3
Figs. 210, 212 and 213. Class NEMATODA

Figure 210

Fig. 210. A typical nematode, a Human Hookworm, *Ancylostoma duodenale;* a, entire worm; b, head showing hooks. (After Looss).

Hookworms have been found to be the cause of much loss of health and energy in regions where it is prevalent. The larva often enter through the feet. Better sanitary conditions are helping to relieve this situation.

ROUNDWORMS

2b Very slender, much elongated worms about the same diameter throughout. Never tapering at posterior end. No lateral lines.

Class NEMATOMORPHA

Fresh Water and terrestrial species (the so-called horse-hair snakes; found in water or within the bodies of insects, etc.)

Order GORDIOIDEA

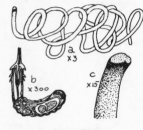

Fig. 211. *Paragordius varius;* a, adult worm; b, embryo; c, head of adult.

Many children have tried raising these "snakes" by putting pieces of horse-hair in water. The theory of spontaneous generation was disproved by scientists many years ago but myths like this are hard to kill.

Figure 211

3a Egg bearing organ of female, a two or more branched tube. Parasitic in animals or in plants or free living. A large majority of the members of this class belong here.　　　　**Order TELOGONIA**

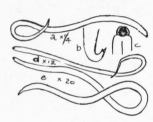

Fig. 212. Eelworm, *Ascaris,* a common intestinal parasite of pig, man, etc.; b, tail of male enlarged; c, head enlarged; d, *Filaria,* the round worm causing elephantiasis; e, *Dolichodorus.*

Round worms are exceedingly abundant. The parasitic species produce immense numbers of eggs which are readily picked up from the soil by domestic animals or even children and a heavy infestation resulting.

Figure 212

3b Egg bearing organ of female, an unbranched tube. Parasitic in warm blooded animals.　　　　**Order HOLOGONIA**

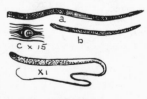

Fig. 213. Trichina (alternates between hog and man), *Trichinella spiralis;* a, female; b, male; c, encysted in muscle of host; d, Whipworm, *Trichuris trichiura* (common intestinal parasite of man).

It seems that Trichina is again increasing in seriousness as a parasite of man. The more frequent practice of feeding hogs on garbage collected in the cities completes the cycle of this dangerous and painful pest. Pork should always be thoroughly cooked.

Figure 213

KEY TO THE CLASSES AND MORE IMPORTANT ORDERS OF THE PHYLUM ROTIFERA

1a With external cilia. Figs. 215-217. 2

1b Without external cilia. All species, minute marine worms.
Class KINORHYNCHA
Order ECHINODERA

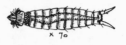

Figure 214

Fig. 214. *Echinoderes dujardini.*
These sea-goers are all less than one-half mm in length. They are characterized by a ring of hooks around the mouth. The sexes are separate.

2a Cilia at anterior end; internal jaws evident. Figs. 216 and 217....3
Class ROTATORIA

2b External cilia only on ventral surface. (No internal jaws).
Class GASTROTRICHA
Without cement tube at hind end of body.
Order CHAETONOTOIDEA

Figure 215

Fig. 215. *Chaetonotus.*
These tiny worm-like forms are found only in fresh water. The sexes are united.

3a Females having only a single ovary (a). Males (minute degenerate forms) usually present.   Order MONOGONONTA

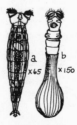

Figure 216

Fig. 216. *Melicerta;* a, female in case; b, male.
The species of this order usually live in tubes of their own construction. Many are attached but a few are free-swimming.
About a dozen families, with more than 200 species have been described.

3b Females with paired ovaries (a). Males unknown.
Order BDELLOIDEA

Figure 217

Fig. 217. a,. *Rotifera citrinus;* b, *Callidina angusticollis.*
It is rare for the members of this order to live in tubes. They creep by and end-to-end motion and swim freely with their ciliated crowns.

KEY TO THE CLASSES AND MORE IMPORTANT ORDERS OF THE PHYLUM BRYOZOA

1a Minute forms having tentacles always exposed, without power of withdrawing them into the body covering. Mouth and anus both opening within the ring of tentacles.　　　**Class ENTOPROCTA**

Fig. 218. *Pedicellina* sp.

Some specialists would make a separate phylum, Calyssozoa for this small group. They are found in both salt and fresh water and are sometimes highly abundant.

Figure 218

1b Having power to withdraw tentacles within body covering (zooecium). Figs. 219-222. 2

2a Piece supporting tentacles (lophophore) circular. (Usually marine)..3

Fig. 219. *Bugula turrita*, single zooecium.

The members of the Bryozoa were thought to be plants by the early scientists. There are around 2000 known species. Only a comparatively few frequent fresh water.

Figure 219

2b Piece supporting tentacles (a): horseshoe shaped or oval. (Confined to fresh water).　　　　　**Order PHYLACTOLAEMATA**

Fig. 220. *Plumatella fungosa* (diagram).

Branched forms are common in this order. They feed on microscopic organisms, diatoms appearing frequently in their diet.

Four families with some 40 species are included in this order.

Figure 220

3a Opening of body covering (zooecium) without an operculum (lid).
Order CYCLOSTOMATA

Fig. 221. *Crisia eburnea;* widely distributed.
The species used here forms white tufts as much as an inch in height. It is rather widely distributed on both of our coasts.
Fifteen families have been described.

Figure 221

3b Opening of zooecium with an operculum. Figs. 222 and 223. 4

4a Operculum membranous. **Order CHILOSTOMATA**

Fig. 222. *Enrystomella bilabiata.*
This is the largest order of the phylum. They range from low-growing forms to colonies almost a foot high.

Figure 222

4b Operculum of setae resembling a comb. Order CTENOSTOMATA

Fig. 223. *Bowerbankia pustulosa.*
The colonies found here while much branched lie in a reclin-ing position. The species pictured inhabits the Pacific Coast. Other species of this genus are found in the Atlantic.

Figure 223

KEY TO THE ORDERS OF THE PHYLUM BRACHIPODA

1a Having a hinge to unite the two parts of the shell.
Order TESTICARDINES

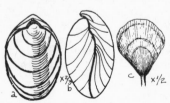

Fig. 224. a, *Magellania,* top view; b, side view; c, *Terebratulina,* side view.
This phylum has long since seen its best day. The fossil species greatly outnumber the living ones. They usual-ly inhabit shallow water.

Figure 224

1b No hinge to unite the parts of the shell. Order ECARDINES

Figure 225

Fig. 225. *Lingula* (from General Biological Supply House). This species inhabits the Pacific and Indian Oceans.

KEY TO THE CLASSES AND ORDERS OF THE PHYLUM ECHINODERMATA

1a Body with radiating arms. Figs. 226-232. 2

1b Body without radiating arms (but sometimes with fleshy tentacles surrounding the mouth). Figs. 233-239. 7

2a Arms with small feathery branches called pinnules; oral (mouth) surface directed upward. Attached to the sea bottom by a stalk during their youth or throughout life. (Sea Lilies, Feather Stars).
Class CRINOIDEA*
Order NEO-CRINOIDEA

Figure 226

Fig. 226. a, An attached crinoid or "Sea Lily" *Pentacrinus*; b, *Antedon*, an unattached, free swimming crinoid.
The known species of extinct Crinoids greatly exceed the living species.

2b Arms without pinnules. Oral surface directed downward. (Never attached by stalk). Figs. 228-232. 3

3a Oral surface of each arm, with a deep groove radiating from the mouth. (Star Fish). Figs. 228-230. 4
Class ASTEROIDEA

---

* This book confines itself to **living** things and has made no effort to show the many groups of plants and animals now known only by fossils. Pieces of stems and parts of heads of fossil Crinoids are so commonly found and enquired about that some of these parts are here pictured.

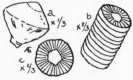

Figure 227

Fig. 227. a, Head (worn by erosion); b, portion of stem, side view; c, stem, end view.

3b Arms without groove as in 3a. Figs. 231 and 232. Brittle Stars and Basket Stars). 6
Class **OPIUROIDEA**

4a Starfishes with either one or two rows of adjoining marginal plates along sides of arms.   Order **PHANEROZONIA**

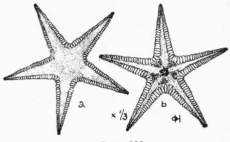

Figure 228

Fig. 228. *Astropecten* sp.; a, aboral (dorsal) view; b, oral view with mouth at center. This genus is widely scattered and has many species, some of which are very prolific.
The species here pictured occur in immense numbers along the Altantic Coast. .

4b Starfish — without marginal plates. Figs. 229 and 230. 5

5a Pedicellariae (microscopic pincer-like parts among the spines) rare or absent, but never with stalks.   Order **SPINULOSA**

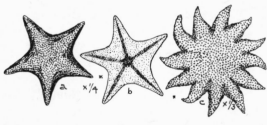

Figure 229

Fig. 229. a, *Asterina*, aboral view; b, oral view; c, "Common Sunstar" *Solaster papposus*.
Five is the most frequent number of rays, but some species have 30 or more arms.

5b Pedicellariae present and stalked (p).   Order **FORCIPULATA**

Figure 230

Fig. 230. *Asterias vulgaris;* p, stalked pedicellarium.
This species is common along the northern Atlantic coast. All Star Fish readily regenerate lost parts.
While these Star Fish appear in shallow water, they may also live at great depth up to half a mile.

SEA URCHINS, ETC.

6a Arms unbranched. (Brittle Stars).   **Order OPHIURAE**

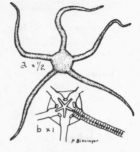

Fig. 231. "Brittle Star"; a, top (aboral) view; b, oral view.

Brittle Stars swim with snake-like movements. Their arms are highly flexible. This is the largest order of the phylum.

Figure 231

6b Arms usually branched. (Basket Stars).   **Order EURYALAE**

Fig. 232. *Gorgonocephalus.*
The basket stars or basket fish have much branched arms which can be rolled in towards the mouth. Their outer covering is softer than that of most of the Echinoderms.

Figure 232

7a Body elongated, soft, cylindrical or 5-sided, (sometimes worm-like). Mouth surrounded by tentacles. (Sea Cucumbers). Figs. 236-239. 10
                                      Class HOLOTHURIOIDEA

7b Body disk shaped, heart shaped or globular. Shell rigid with close fitting plates. (Cake Urchins, Heart Urchins and Sea Urchins). Figs. 233-235. 8
                                        Class ECHINOIDEA

8a Mouth centrally located. Figs. 234 and 235. 9

8b Neither mouth (m) nor anus (a) centrally located. No prominent teeth. (Heart Urchins, etc.)   **Order SPATANGOIDA**

Fig. 233. a Heart Urchin, *Echinocardium*; b, dorsal view; c, ventral view showing mouth (m) and anal opening (a); d, side view. Some 60 genera with 150 species fall here.

Figure 233

86

**9a Anus at edge. Shell usually disk-like and much flattened.
(Cake Urchins or Sand Dollars). Order CLYPEASTROIDA**

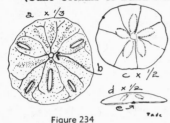

Fig. 234. a, Keyhole Urchin, *Mellita*, oral view; b, mouth; c, Sand Dollar, *Echinarachnius*, aboral view; d, edge view; e, anus.
Their very thin shells make the members of this group highly interesting. They would seem to offer very little room within for the living animals.

Figure 234

**9b Anus in center of aboral surface. Shell more or less globular.
(Sea Urchins).**

Order ENDOCYCLICA

Fig. 235. *Arbacia*, oral (lower) view.
The spines of the sea urchins are in some species quite long. They are attached by a ball and socket joint and are moved at will by the animal. Some European countries use Sea Urchins for food.

Figure 235

**10a Tentacles shield shaped. Feet numerous on ventral side; dorsal
side with conical papillae. Order ASPIDOCHIROTA**

Fig. 236. *Stichopus californicus*.
Sea Cucumbers are consumed in large numbers in the Orient.

Figure 236

10b Tentacles tree-like, linear or feather-like. 11

11a Tentacles tree-like, feet numerous. Order DENDROCHIROTA

Fig. 237. *Cucumaria curata*.
The order includes more than 200 species. They are often found in shallow water.

Figure 237.

**11b Tentacles linear or feather-like; no feet with possible exception
of anal papillae. Figs. 238 and 239. ....12**

12a Smooth thick-skinned form, barrel shaped with tapering tail. Tentacles small, usually 15 in a circle around the mouth.

Order MOLPADONIA

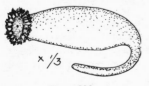

Fig. 238. *Caudina arenata*.
When attacked sea cucumbers break off parts which are readily regenerated.

Figure 238

12b Body worm-like; tentacles feather-like; skin thin, more or less transparent. (No feet).   Order APODA

Figure 239

Fig. 239. *Leptosynapta albicans.*
Some large specimens attain a length of 8 inches or more.

KEY TO THE CLASSES AND MORE IMPORTANT ORDERS OF THE PHYLUM MOLLUSCA

1a With a distinct head. Figs. 242-244, 249 and 250. 2

1b Without a distinct head. Figs. 245-248. 3

2a Head terminating in a horny beak surrounded by 8 or more long arms. (Squids, Cuttle Fish, Devil Fish, etc.). Figs. 249 and 250.....8
                          Class CEPHALOPODA

2b Head without long arms, but with one or two pairs of fleshy tentacles. Naked or with coiled or cone-like shell. (Snails, etc.). Figs. 242-244. 5
                          Class GASTROPODA

3a Shell of two distinct parts (bivalve). Oysters, Clams, Scallops, Cockels, etc. Figs. 245-248. 7
                          Class PELECYPODA

3b Not having a bivalve shell. Figs. 240 and 241. 4

4a Upper side covered with a shell of eight plates or animals without a shell.   Class AMPHINEURA
With shell. (The Chitons).   Order POLYPLACOPHORA

Figure 240

Fig. 240. A Chiton; a, dorsal view; b, ventral view.
Many chitons are only an inch or less in length but a few species attain a length of nearly a foot.

4b Shell cylindrical or tusk shaped.   Class SCAPHOPODA

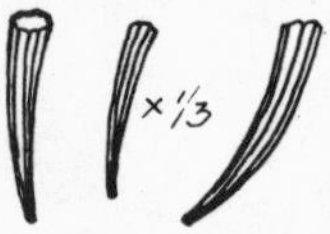

Figure 241

Fig. 241. One order. *Dentalium*; marine.
The Japanese are using shells of this class to make tails to some of the shell birds seen in souvenir shops. It offers a way to get some specimens at small cost.

MOLLUSKS

5a Snails and slugs living on land or in fresh water; usually with shell but never with an operculum. Breathe by means of lungs; without gills. Order PULMONATA

Fig. 242. a, *Helix*; b, c, *Planorbis*; d, *Lymnaea*; e, *Limax*, a slug.

Some slugs are serious plant pests. Their slimy exterior makes them annoying to handle.

Don't expect land snails to stay in an aquarium. A cat doesn't like it either.

Figure 242

5b Not as in 5a. 6

6a Naked or with small shells; wholly marine. Order OPISTHOBRANCHIATA

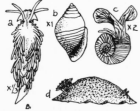

Fig. 243. a, A Sea Slug, *Aeolis*; b, *Acteon*; c, *Spiratella*; d, A Nudibranch, *Doris*.

The Sea Slugs are often much branched. These snails usually live along the shore. Many are brilliantly colored.

Figure 243

6b Mostly marine snails; limpets, abalones, etc.; frequently of large size. Almost always with a shell and operculum. Often brilliantly colored and attractively marked. Order PROSOBRANCHIATA

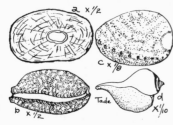

Fig. 244. a, Keyhole Limpet, *Fissurella*; b, Cowrie, *Cypraea*; c, Abalone, *Haliotis*; d, *Busycon*.

The Abalones have considerable commercial value. Buttons and ornaments are made from the shells, while the fleshy part of the animal is a favorite article of food.

Figure 244

7a Wholly marine; gills but short flattened pinnate leaflets, extending to rear in mantle cavity. Order PROTOBRANCHIATA

Fig. 245. a, Diagram showing arrangement of gills (g) and mantle (m); b, *Yoldia*; c, *Solemya*. These two genera of which there are several species are widely distributed.

Figure 245

89

7b Wholly marine; gills consist of two paired rows of long filaments hanging down into mantle cavity and recurving.

Order FILIBRANCHIATA

Figure 246

Fig. 246. a, Diagramatic cross section showing arrangement of gills (g); mantle (m); and foot (f); b, Edible mussel, *Mytilus edulis*.

As the name indicates the species pictured here is much used for food in Europe.

7c Both fresh water and marine forms. Two continuous plate-like gills on each side. Usually two adductor muscles. (A very large order).

Order EULAMELLIBRANCHIATA

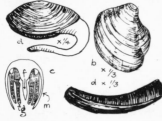

Figure 247

Fig. 247. a, Long Clam, *Mya arenaria*; b, *Unio* sp.; c, cross section showing gills (g), foot (f) and mantle (m); d, Razor clam, *Ensis directus*.

Razor clams live in shallow ocean water. Some species are very abundant. They are prized as food.

7d Wholly marine. Gills often connected with each other. Usually but one adductor muscle. Shells often of unequal size. Foot weak or absent.

Order PSEUDOLAMELLIBRANCHIATA

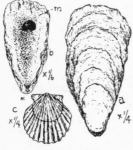

Figure 248

Fig. 248. "The American Oyster", *Ostrea virginica*; a, outside of shell; b, inside view of shell showing muscle scar (m); c, Common Scallop, *Pecten irradians*.

Oyster fishing is one of the major industries of the coast and numerous regulations have become necessary. Oysters produce pearls.

8a No ink sac. Shell external and coiled; about half of it divided by partitions into gas filled compartments. (The Chambered Nautilus, etc.)

Order TETRABRANCHIATA

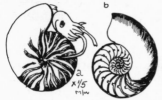

Figure 249

Fig. 249. "The Pearly Nautilus." *Nautilus pompilius*. Pacific Ocean. a, Shell with living animal; b, Split shell showing chambers and passage way leading to center.

8b Ink sac present. Shell usually wholly internal or without shell. (Squids, Cuttle Fish and Devil Fish). Order **DEBRANCHIATA**

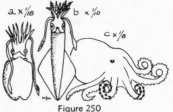

Fig. 250. a, Cuttle Fish, *Sepia officinalis*; b, Common Squid, *Loligo pealei*; c, Devil Fish, *Octopus bairdii*.

Figure 250

The usual length of Squids and Cuttle Fish ranges from a few inches to two or three feet but the Giant Squid (*Architeuthis princeps*), an apparently world wide deep sea species has a body length of 20 feet, to which may be added 35 feet of arm length. It is by all odds the largest known mollusk.

KEY TO THE MORE COMMON CLASSES AND ORDERS OF THE PHYLUM ANNELIDA

A June-bug married an Angle Worm. | An accident cut her in two. | They arrested the bug for bigamy. | Now what could the poor fellow do?

1a Disk-like sucker at each end. Body usually flattened and showing segments. Figs. 255 and 256. 6
(Leeches). Class **HIRUDINEA**

1b Without suckers. Figs. 251-254, 257 and 258. 2

2a With external bristles for locomotion. (Setae). Figs. 252-254, 257 and 258. 3

2b Without bristles. (Small marine worms).

Class **ARCHIANNELIDA**

Figure 251

But one order.
Fig. 251. *Polygordius*; salmon colored.
All of the members of this order are small worms. Some are greatly reduced, being only a fraction of a millimeter in length. They live among sea weeds.

3a Distinctly segmented. Freshwater, in earth or marine. Figs. 252-254. ....**4**

3b Rather large marine worms with little or no segmentation showing in adults. Figs. 257 and 258. ....**7**
Class GEPHYREA

4a With many setae grouped on fleshy side pads (parapodia). Usually distinct head with appendages. (Mostly marine). Figs. 253 and 254. ....**5**
Class POLYCHAETA

4b No parapodia. No distinct head with appendages. Terrestrial or fresh water. Class OLIGOCHAETA

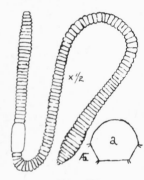

One order with over 2500 species.
Fig. 252. Common Earth-worm, or "Fishing Worm", *Lumbricus terrestris*; a, Outline of cross section showing location of setae.
What would the bare-foot fisher boy do if it were not for this lowly earth-worm? It is interesting to note their ability at regeneration. Cultivating the soil may mutilate the worms but also multiplies them.

Figure 252

5a Free living, usually predacious species. All segments similar.

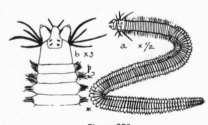

Order POLYCHAETA ERRANTIA
Fig. 253. Clam worm, *Nereis virens*; a, entire worm; b, head and few segments showing *parapodia* (p).
During the breeding season these sand worms collect at night in large numbers at the ocean's surface. Quantities of them may then be taken easily.

Figure 253

5b Burrowing or tube living forms. Order POLYCHAETA SEDENTARIA

Fig. 254. *Amphitrite ornata;* a pinkish worm living in tubes in the sand in shallow marine situations.
Many marine worms belong here. The apical part of many species with its prominent tuft of tentacles is in evidence while the remainder of the animal reposes in its burrow.

Figure 254

SEGMENTED WORMS

6a Leeches with jaws; body rings five; blood red; fresh water or terrestrial. **Order GNATHOBDELLIDA**

Figure 255

Fig. 255. Medicinal Leech, *Hirudo medicinalis.*
This animal was once in constant association with the best medical men and visited the homes of rich and poor alike. Times changed and it is now little more than a tramp.

6b No jaws but with a proboscis, which can be extended from mouth; body rings 3 or 4; blood colorless; both fresh water and marine forms. **Order RHYNCHOBDELLIDA**

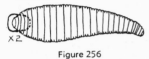

Figure 256

Fig. 256. Leech, *Glossiphonia elegans.*
Turtles and many other aquatic animals may be found with leeches attached. This offers one good means of collecting them.

7a Marine worms with setae and prominent proboscis.
Order ECHIURIDA

Figure 257

Fig. 257. *Echiurus;* a, setae; b, proboscis.
The members of this and of the following order are of apparently little importance and are known only to scientists.

7b Without setae; body robust, without tentacles. **Order PRIAPULIDA**

Figure 258

Fig. 258. *Priapulus.*
These animals were once thought to be related to the sea cucumbers.

KEY TO THE CLASSES OF THE PHYLUM ARTHROPODA

1a Aquatic arthropods breathing by means of gills. Figs. 264-268, 308-313, etc. 2

1b Air breathing arthropods. No gills in evidence. Figs. 271-279, 322-324, 330-333, etc. 3

2a With 2 pair of antennae. Figs. 261-270.
Class CRUSTACEA p. 94

93

2b With 1 pair of antennae. Figs. 308-311, etc.

Class INSECTA (in part) pp. 98 and 109

2c Without antennae. (The King Crab). Fig. 326.

Class ARACHNIDA (in part) p. 116

3a With seven thoracic segments each bearing a pair of legs; two pair of antennae (the first very small).

Class CRUSTACEAE (in part)
Order ISOPODA

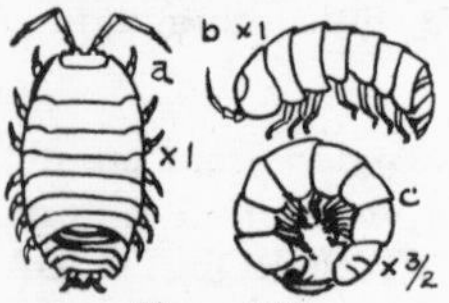

Fig. 259. a, Snow Bug, *Oniscus*, dorsal view; b and c, Pill Bug, *Armadillidium*, in damp places, widely distributed.

Figure 259

3b With one pair of antennae. Figs. 288-294, etc. 4

3c Without antennae. Usually eight legs. Never with wings. Figs. 326-336.   Class ARACHNIDA, p. 116

4a Body worm-like. Figs. 271-273, 317-324, etc. 5

4b Body divided into head, thorax and abdomen with 3 pairs of legs (legs are jointed and attached to thorax); with or without wings. Figs. 281-286, 315, 316, etc.   Class INSECTA (Hexopoda) p. 98

5a Body without external segments. Rather unusual tropical or semi-tropical forms. But one order, 2 families and about 75 species.

Class ONYCHOPHORA

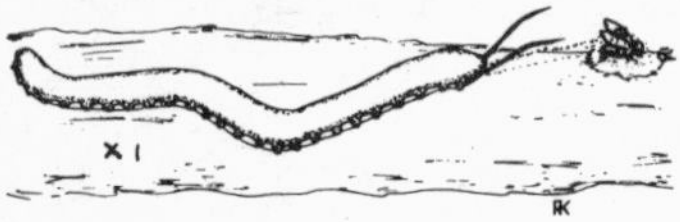

Fig. 260. *Peripatus* "Shooting a fly with slime".

These animals are highly interesting to the scientist but they are of scant economic importance.

Figure 260

5b Body plainly segmented. 6

6a With from 9 to almost 200 pairs of legs. All legs jointed and similar. Figs. 271-273.   Class MYRIOPODA p. 97

6b With 0 or 3 pairs of jointed legs on thoracic region and with 0 to 9 pairs of pro-legs (fleshy structures each with many hooks) on the abdomen. Figs. 317-320, 322-324, etc.

Class INSECTA (Immature stages) p. 109

KEY TO THE MORE IMPORTANT ORDERS OF THE CLASS CRUSTACEAE

1a Small forms (usually less than ½ inch in length) often minute; with no abdominal appendages. Figs. 261-264. 2

Subclass, ENTOMOSTRACA

1b Larger forms usually with abdominal appendages. Figs. 265-270.

.... 4

2a Body of animal enclosed in a limy shell and attached (barnacles), or parasitic on mollusks or other crustacea.

Order CIRRIPEDIA

Figure 261

Fig. 261. a, Goose Barnacle, *Lepas anatifera*; Common Barnacle, *Balanus*.
Barnacles make a sharp addition to the normal expense of ship maintenance. They attach themselves to the hulls and multiply rapidly. To remove them is costly, to leave them retards the ship.

2b Free swimming, or parasitic on fish and a few other animals. Figs. 262-264. 3

3a Appendages of thorax flat and leaf-like for respiration and swimming.

Order BRANCHIOPODA

Figure 262

Fig. 262. *Daphnia*.
The members of this order are largely confined to fresh water. They are usually less than an inch in length. Many species are much smaller.

3b Either free swimming, parasitic or living in mud and sand. The free living forms elongated and segmented. Thoracic appendages cylindric.

Order COPEPODA

Figure 263

Fig. 263. *Cyclops viridis*, with egg sacs, (a).
Cyclops is famous for its one eye. In fact the two eyes have met at the median line and fused. They are often exceedingly numerous and play an important part in making food for other aquatic animals.

3c Body laterally compressed, showing no segmentation and wholly enclosed in a two valved carapace.

Order OSTRACODA

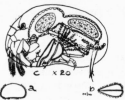

Figure 264

Fig. 264. *Eucypris virens*; a, side view of shell; b, ventral view of shell; c, animal in shell. Widely distributed.
The large majority of members of this order are marine. They, too, often have one median eye. More than one thousand species are known.

4a Carapace covering the entire thorax. Tribe EUCARIDA.
(Shrimps, Crayfish, Lobsters, Crabs).   **Order DECAPODA**

Fig. 265. a, A Crab, *Cancer*, marine; b, Marine Shrimp, *Crago*; c, Freshwater Crayfish, *Cambarus*.
The Lobster is the giant of this group of largest crustacea. The hermit crabs which have lived for so many generations in borrowed snail shells that they now know no other way, always command interest.

Figure 265

4b Carapace not covering entire thorax. (Sometimes wanting).

5a Abdomen wider than the small cephalothorax. (But one order).
     Tribe, HOPLOCARIDA
     Order STOMATOPODA

Fig. 266. *Squilla empusa*.
This animal is very much flattened. This character together with its broad abdomen makes it look radically different from most crustaceans.

Figure 266

5b Abdomen never wider than the cephalothorax.
     Tribe, PERACARIDA

6a Head and thorax only partly covered with a shell (carapace).

6b Without carapace.

7a Posterior appendages all two parted.   **Order MYSIDACEA**

Fig. 267. *Mysis*, fresh water.
These animals are usually somewhat transparent. About 300 species are known, mostly marine.

Figure 267

7b Not all the posterior appendages two-parted. Abdomen long and slender.   **Order CUMACEA**

Fig. 268. *Diastylis*, Northern Atlantic Ocean.
Nearly all of the some 400 species of this order are marine and live in sand and mud along the shore.

Figure 268

8a Body flattened on sides, (compressed).   Order **AMPHIPODA**

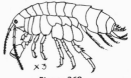

Figure 269

Fig. 269. *Hyalella*. Fresh water.
Here is another large order of more than two thousand known species almost all of which are marine.

8b Body flattened on top and bottom (depressed).   Order **ISOPODA**
(In part) (See also page 94)

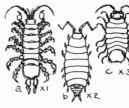

Figure 270

Fig. 270. a, *Asellus communis*; fresh water; b, *Metaponorthus*, a land form; c, *Jaera*, a marine species.
The aquatic members of this group are only "more crustaceans" to the casual observer. The land forms are distinctive and as "sow bugs" are known to all.

KEY TO THE MORE COMMON ORDERS OF THE CLASS MYRIOPODA

1a Most of the body segments with two pairs of legs to each. Body usually round in cross section. Animals coil as a helical spring when disturbed. (The Millipedes or Thousand Legged Worms).
         Order **DIPLOPODA**

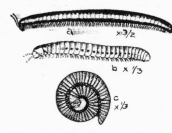

Figure 271

Fig. 271. a, *Parajulus* (U. S. D. A.); b, c, *Spirobolus*, traveling and coiled as when disturbed.
Millipedes are plant feeders and are not poisonous. They are often mistaken for wire worms.

CENTIPEDES, ETC.

1b Only one pair of legs to each segment. Figs. 272 and 273. 2
2a Minute colorless animals. Legs, 12 pairs; each with 2 claws.

Order SYMPHYLA

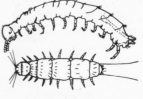

Figure 272

Fig. 272. a, Sentigerella; b, Pauropus.
Some of the members of this order are fairly common under stones. They run actively when disturbed. They are all very small and for that reason are poorly known except to specialists.

2b Larger than 2a with 15 to almost 200 pairs of legs, body compressed (oval in cross section). Usually run rapidly when disturbed. (The Centipedes or Hundred Legged Worms.)

Order CHILOPODA

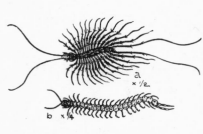

Figure 273

Fig. 273. a, House Centipede, Scutigera forceps (U. S. D. A.); b, Scolopendra.
The known number of species of centipedes runs around a thousand. They range in size from small, very slender ones to species more than a foot in length. The bite of the larger ones is poisonous and dangerous to man. House centipedes are quite inoffensive and serve a good purpose in killing flies and other insects.

KEY TO THE MORE IMPORTANT ORDERS OF THE CLASS INSECTA*

1a Insects with wings. Figs. 274-289. 2
1b Insects having no wings or only rudimentary wings. Figs. 290-305. 17

* These keys are made for the determination of adult insects. Immature forms of all orders are wingless. See page 105 for key to the orders of immature stages.

98

2a Insects with only one pair of thin, usually transparent wings; the second pair replaced with short pin-like structures (balancers). (Flies, mosquitos, etc.) **Order DIPTERA**

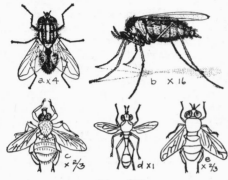

Fig. 274. a, The Common House Fly, *Musca domestica*; b, The Rose Midge. — (U. S. D. A.); c, An Assasin Fly; d, *Physocephala*; e, A Horsefly, *Tabanus*.

Several orders have an occasional species in which one pair of wings is missing. The absence of balancers will prove that they are not Diptera.

Figure 274

2b Insects with two pairs of wings. Figs. 275-289. 3

3a The two pair of wings unlike in structure (first pair thick and horny as in the beetles; leathery at the base with overlapping membraneous tips as in the true bugs or leathery and with veins as in the grasshoppers). Figs. 275-278. 4

3b The two pair of wings of similar structure and with about the same degree of thickness (as in the bees, butterflies, dragonflies, etc.). (One pair is often colored and would thus differ from the other in transparency.) Figs. 279-289. 7

4a Outer (first) pair of wings of hard horn-like substance and meeting in a straight line down the back (as in the beetles and earwigs). Figs. 275 and 276. 5

4b Wings not as in 4a. Figs. 277 and 278. 6

5a With a prominent pair of pincer-like parts (a) at tip of abdomen (Earwigs). Fig. 275. **Order DERMAPTERA**

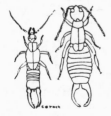

Fig. 275. Two Earwigs.
They fly well although they do not look like it. The wings are folded under the short elytra. They are said to attack the ears of man, but that is another fake nature yarn.

Figure 275

5b Without large pincers at the end of the abdomen. (Beetles).

Order COLEOPTERA

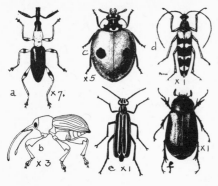

Figure 276

Fig. 276. a, Sweet Potato Weevil; b, Chestnut Weevil, (Family Curculionidae); c, The Two-spot Lady Beetle, *Adalia bipunctata*, (Family Coccinellidae); d, *Typocerus velutina*, (Family Cerambycidae); e, a Blister Beetle, (Family Meloidae); f, a May Beetle, (Family Scarabaeidae), (U. S. D. A.).

This is the most numerous order of insects or of Living Things. More than 200,000 species of beetles are known to science.

6a Front wings leathery at their base (a), membranous and overlapping at their tips (b); mouth parts a tube for sucking, usually extending from underside of head in backward direction. (True Bugs).

Order HEMIPTERA

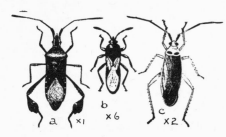

Figure 277

Fig. 277. a, The Northern Leaf-footed Plant-bug, *Leptoglossus oppositus*; b, Chinch-bug; *Blissus leucopterus*; Cotton Leaf-bug, *Calocoris rapidus*, (U. S. D. A.).

This is a large order and includes some of our most destructive insects. Many of them are protected by vile odors which they emit when disturbed.

6b Front wings leathery, with veins; hind wings folded lengthwise. Mouth parts for chewing. (Crickets, Roaches, Katydids, Grasshoppers, etc.)

Order ORTHOPTERA

Figure 278

Fig. 278. The Australian Cockroach, *Periplaneta australasiae*; b, Katydid, *Scudder furcata*; c, Field Cricket, *Gryllus assimilis*; d, A grasshopper or locust, *Encoptolophus sordidus costalis*.

7a Wings covered with scales (in a few species with transparent areas). Mouth parts a coiled tube for sucking (Moths and Butter-flies). **Order LEPIDOPTERA**

Figure 279

Fig. 279. a, Peach Tree Borer (a clear wing moth), *Aegeria exitiosa;* b, Black Swallowtail Butterfly, *Papilio polyxenes.* c, Armyworm Moths, *Cirphis unipuncta,* (U. S. D. A.).

Adults of this order are beautiful to collect and rather inoffensive in their food habits. Many species, however, are exceedingly destructive while in the growing stage (caterpillars).

7b Wings transparent or thinly clothed with hairs (as in Bees, May-flies, Dragonflies, etc.). Figs. 280-289. 8

8a Mouth parts a tube for sucking, attached to hinder part of the lower surface of the head. Wings when at rest sloping down and outward from center, thus ∧ (Cicadas, Leafhoppers, Treehoppers, Aphids, etc.). **Order HOMOPTERA**

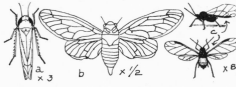

Figure 280

Fig. 280. a, The Potato Leaf-hopper, (Family Cicadellidae), b, a *Cicada,* (Family Cicadidae); c, The Melon *Aphid,* (Family Aphididae).

The members of this order are from medium sized to small insects with the exception of the cicadas or so-called "Locusts", many of which are large.

8b Not as in 8a. Figs. 281-289. 9

9a Slender moth-like insects with long slim antennae; no mouth parts in evidence except a pair of slender palpi (a). Wings frequently hairy: usually broadest beyond the middle. (Caddis-flies). **Order TRICHOPTERA**

Figure 281

Fig. 281. A Typical Caddis-fly. a, adult; b, larva in its case.
These insects, most of which are small are often mistaken for moths. They appear in immense numbers at lights during the summer months. The larvae are aquatic.

9b Not as in 9a. Figs. 283-289. 10

10a Wings with but few cross veins (or none) as in the bees and thrips. Figs. 282 and 283. 11

10b Wings with many cross veins, as in the dragon flies, Mayflies, lacewings, etc. Figs. 284-289. 12

11a Front wings the larger; hind wings often hooked to front wings. Mouth parts for chewing, or for chewing and sucking. (Bees, Wasps, Ants, etc.).   Order **HYMENOPTERA**

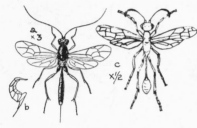

Fig. 282. a, An Ichenumon wasp, *Limneria;* b, Side view of abdomen of female; c, Muddauber Wasp, *Sceliphron coementarium*, (U. S. D. A.).

The highly developed community life of some species of this order, rivals that of man. Many of the members of this order are highly beneficial.

Figure 282

11b Very small, slender insects. Wings very narrow and margined with bristly hairs. (Thrips).   Order **THYSANOPTERA**

Fig. 283. Onion Thrips, *Thrips tabaci.*
All thrips are small. They have peculiar sucking mouth parts and live on plant juices. Like many other insects, they are good botanists and make no mistake in selecting the right species of plant on which to lay their eggs. The young closely resemble the adults but have no wings.

Figure 283

12a Front wings much larger than hind wings. Wings when at rest held vertically above body. Long fragile pointed tails behind. (Mayflies).   Order **EPHEMERIDA**

Fig. 284. A May-fly, *Hexagenia limbata.*
We've heard the public speakers refer in an illustration to the "May-fly, which dies within twenty-four hours from the time it is born." Insects make their last molt, emerge from the pupa or hatch from the egg; but a few could be said to be "born". May-flies do have a very short life in their adult stage but it should be kept in mind that this is preceded by months and in some species years of development in the nymph stage in the water.

Figure 284

12b Not as in 12a. Figs. 285-289. 13

13a Head prolonged into a trunk-like beak with chewing mouth parts at its tip. (Scorpion flies). Order MECOPTERA

Fig. 285. a, A Scorpionfly, *Panorpa*, sp.; b, *Bittacus*, sp.

The members of this second genus roughly resemble crane flies but possess two pairs of wings. They are occasionally found quite abundant in dense woods near water, where their larvae develop. The adults hang suspended by their front legs to the undersides of shrubs and catch with their hind legs, insects that come within their reach, for this is their food.

Figure 285

13b Not as in 13a. Figs. 286-289. 14

14a Antennae short and inconspicuous; long slender insects with long narrow wings. (Damsel flies and Dragon flies).

Order ODONATA

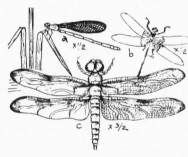

Fig. 286. Damsel flies; a, at rest; b, in flight; c, Dragon fly at rest, *Libellula pulchella*. (Gen. Biol. Supply Co.).

Damsel flies are slender and fold their wings together when at rest while dragon flies are heavier and hold their wings in a plane at right angles to the body when they alight.

Figure 286

14b Antennae readily seen. Figs. 287-289. 15

15a Abdomen usually with two short tails (a). Back wings broader than front wings and folded length-wise. (Stone flies).

Order PLECOPTERA

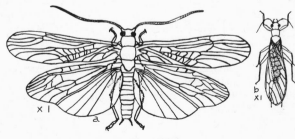

Fig. 287. a, A Stone Fly with wings spread, *Perla* sp.; b, at rest, *Neoperla clymene*.

These insects may be found flying to lights in the neighborhood of water courses. The larvae are aquatic and have an important relation in furnishing food for fish.

Figure 287

15b Not as in 15a. Figs. 288 and 289. 16

16a No appendages at end of abdomen. Tarsi with five segments. (Ant Lions, Lacewings, Dobson flies, etc.).   Order NEUROPTERA

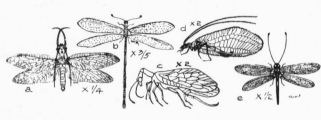

Figure 288

Fig. 288. a, Dobson Fly, *Corydalis cornuta;* b, adult of Ant Lion, *Hesperoleon;* c, *Raphidia* sp.; d, Lacewing, *Chrysopa,* sp.;

e, an Ascalaphid, *Ulolodes macleayana.* The Lacewings are most numerous in this order and the most important economically. Their larvae are highly destructive to plant lice.

16b Wings equal in size and with indistinct veins. Thorax in front of wings very short. (Termites or White Ants).   Order ISOPTERA

Figure 289

Fig. 289. A Young Termite Queen, *Reticulitermes flavipes.*
It is only the males and the queens which have wings. Even the latter break off their wings when they are ready to establish a colony. Males are short-lived.

17a Narrow waisted, ant-like insects. (Ants, Velvet Ants, etc.).
                                        Order HYMENOPTERA

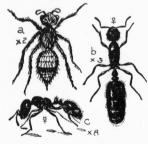

Figure 290

Fig. 290. a, A Velvet Ant, *Dasymutilla* sp.; b, Little Black Ant (Queen); c, Worker, *Monomorium minimum.*
Ants are abundant everywhere and represent many different species. Females or the Velvet ants are wingless. They sting viciously.

17b Not narrow waisted. Figs. 291-305. 18

18a Ant-like but with abdomen broadly joined to thorax. Not flattened. Usually light colored. (White Ants or Termites).

Order ISOPTERA

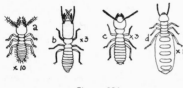

Figure 291

Fig. 291. White Ants, *Reticulitermes flavipes;* a, freshly hatched nymph; b, soldier; c, common worker; d, egg laying female.
Termites avoid light and do not go out of their burrows except when the queens and males swarm.

18b Not as in 18a. Figs. 292-305. 19

19a Small, flat bodied insects with heads as wide as bodies or nearly so. (Chewing mouth parts). Figs. 292 and 293. 20

19b Not as in 19a. Figs. 294-305. 21

20a Antennae of many segments. Found on old papers, moss, etc. (Book-lice, Bark-lice, etc.). **Order CORRODENTIA**

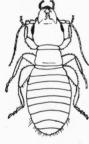

Figure 292

Fig. 292. A Book Louse, *Atropos* sp.
The "book worm" will frequently see these interesting tiny creatures running across his pages as he burns his midnight hundred watts. The bark lice belong, also, to this order. Some of them are winged and somewhat resemble a winged aphid.

20b Antennae short; not over five segments. Found mostly on birds; a few on mammals. (Bird-lice). **Order MALLOPHAGA**

Figure 293

Fig. 293. The Common Hen Louse, *Menopon pallidum,* (U. S. D. A.).
The bird lice are usually much flattened. They feed on feathers and skin scales. Their damage then is in the annoyance their movements give their unwilling hosts. Their entire life, egg and all, is spent on the bird or mammal host.

21a Small, soft-bodied insects with small heads and plump bodies. Two short tubes extending from back of abdomen (t). Found sucking juice from plants; often attended by ants. (Plant lice or Aphids). Order HOMOPTERA

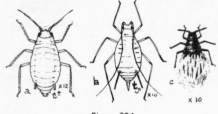

Fig. 294. a, The Corn-Leaf Aphid, *Aphis maidis;* b, Pea Aphid, *Macrosiphum pisi;* c, Woolly Aphid, *Schizoneura lanigera,* (U. S. D. A.).

During much of the year all aphids are females. These "stem mothers" produce living young without being fertilized, often at the rate of eight to ten

Figure 294

offsprings per day. Since these may mature and begin giving birth to young aphids within a week, it is plain why these tiny creatures are such persistent plant pests.

21b Not as in 21a. Figs. 295-305. ....**22**

22a Small; broad and flat across back; fleshy legs, each with single hook-like claw for grasping hairs; beak fleshy and unsegmented. Found only on mammals. (Sucking lice).

Order ANOPLURA

Fig. 295. Short-nosed cattle louse, *Haematopinus eurysternus.*

The members of this order are blood suckers and as such may greatly deplete the strength of their host to say nothing of the disease germs directly transmitted by them. It seems that almost every species of mammal has one or more species of sucking lice which parasite it.

Figure 295

22b Not as in 22a. Figs. 296-305. ....**23**

23a Small narrow insects, flattened on the sides; sucking mouth parts; hind legs for jumping; tarsi with five segments. (Fleas).

Order SIPHONAPTERA

Fig. 296. a, Dog flea, *Ctenocephalus canis;* b, "Jigger" flea or Chigoe, *Dermatophilus penetrans,* (U.S.D.A.). Fleas may be readily recognized by their compressed shape and for their high record in the standing long jump. Unlike lice their life is spent on and off their host.

Figure 296

It is only the adult that feeds on blood; the eggs, larvae and pupae are in no way related to the host of the adult, but are laid and develop wholly apart from it.

23b Not as in 23a. Figs. 297-305. ....**24**

24a Body thickly covered with scales, mouth parts for sucking or absent. (A few female moths). Order **LEPIDOPTERA**

Figure 297

Fig. 297. Female of White Marked Tussock Moth, *Hemerocampa leuscostigma.*

Just why Nature should choose to handicap some of the female moths by depriving them of wings would make a subject for considerable speculation. Larvae of the moth here shown usually pupate on the food plant. When the females emerge they mate and lay their eggs on the cocoon. Fall and Spring Cankerworms pupate in the ground under their food plant. When the wingless females emerge they must climb the tree to lay their eggs. Man has found that he can easily control them by encircling the tree trunks with sticky bands.

24b Not as in 24a. Figs. 298-305. ....**25**

25a Very delicate insects with chewing mouth parts and long, jointed, thread-like tails and antennae. (Fish-moths, Bristle-tails, Fire-brats). Order **THYSANURA**

Figure 298

Fig. 298. The Silverfish, *Lepisma saccharina.*

Some insects have apparently had wings and later lost them. The members of this very small order have never experienced flight. Starches constitute their first choice of food. For that reason they may be found where starched linens or papers are stored. They may even eat the paste from the wall-paper.

25b Not as in 25a. Figs. 299-305. ....**26**

26a Delicate insects with chewing mouth parts and but six abdominal segments. Underside of abdomen frequently has a long, usually double appendage (d) used for leaping. (Spring-tails). Order **COLLEMBOLA**

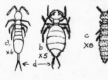

Figure 299

Fig. 299. Three typical spring-tails, a, *Isotoma* sp.; b, *Sminthurus* sp.; c, *Achorates nivicola.* Spring-tails are very abundant in damp places and may be readily found under stones or leaves or under bark on decaying logs.

26b Not as in 26a. Figs. 300-305. ....**27**

27a With mouth parts for chewing. Figs. 300-303. 28

27b With mouth parts for sucking. Figs. 304 and 305. 30

28a Antennae thread-like; face directed forward or downward.
(Crickets, Roaches, Grasshoppers, Walkingsticks).
Order ORTHOPTERA

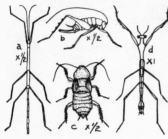

Figure 300

Fig. 300. a, A Walkingstick, *Pseudo-meryle;* b, A Camel Cricket, *Ceutho-philus;* c, Cockroach (female), *Blatta orientalis,* d, Praying Mantis, *Oligonyx.* Many of the members of this order are destructive, some of them highly so. From the time of the plagues of Egypt down to the present time great swarms of grasshoppers (or locusts) have been appearing and consuming every green thing to come within their range.

28b Antennae; (1), bead-like; (2), club-like or (3) comb-like. Figs. 301-303. 29

Figure 301

29a With a prominent pair of movable forceps at tip of abdomen (a). (Earwigs). Order DERMAPTERA

Figure 302

Fig. 302. A Wingless Earwig.
Most earwigs are equipped with a sturdy pair of membranous wings which they fold under their short wing covers much like the Rove beetles; a few species however, like the one here pictured, are flightless.

29b Without prominent forceps at tip of abdomen. Often worm-like. (Beetles). Order COLEOPTERA

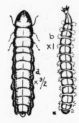

Figure 303

Fig. 303. a, Female Firefly, *Lamphrophorus;* b, A Glow-worm (also a female Firefly), *Phengodes.*
Glow-worms must be seen alive if one is to appreciate their beauty and interest. The color of light they give off varies with different species. Paraguay is the home of one that has been named the "Railway Beetle" since it carries a red light at each end and a series of green ones along its sides.

30a Small legless insects firmly attached to plant leaves or stems. Frequently covered with a waxy scale.
(Scale insects).   Order HOMOPTERA

Figure 304

Fig. 304. a, Maple Scale, *Pulvinaria innumerabilis;* b, San Jose Scale, *Aspidiotus perniciosus;* c, Mealy Bug, *Dactylopius citri,* (U. S. D. A.). These insects h a v e sacrificed their opportunity to travel around and see the world for a constant food supply and comparative security. Their life is surely not very exciting.

30b Well developed legs; sucking beak arising at front of head and held between the legs. (True Bugs).   Order HEMIPTERA

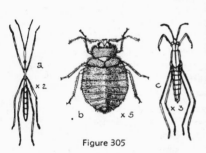

Figure 305

Fig. 305. a, Marsh Treader, *Hydrometra;* b, Bedbug, *Cimex lectularius;* c, A Water Strider.
Many families of this order have some wingless or shortwinged species.

The bedbug also feeds on mice, rabbits, guinea pigs, horses cattle and poultry, but it is a different species that is found in the nests of birds and bats.

KEY TO THE MORE IMPORTANT ORDER OF INSECTS IN THEIR IMMATURE FORMS *

*Immature forms of the following orders so closely resemble the adults that a special key for their identification does not seem necessary — **Thysanura Collembola, Dermaptera, Isoptera, Thysanoptera, Corrodentia, Mallophaga, Anoplura.**

3a With mouth parts combined into a jointed sucking beak on under side of head. (Nymphs of true bugs.) Order HEMIPTERA

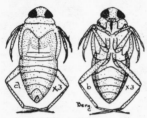

Figure 306

Fig. 306. Nymph of a Back-swimmer, *Notonecta* sp.; a, dorsal view; b, ventral view.

The Water-scorpions, Giant Water-bugs and Water-boatmen are other groups of this order which develop aquatically.

3b With mouth parts fitted for biting and chewing. Figs. 307-309.....4

4a Labium (under lip) capable of being extended a considerable distance in front of head (c). No gills on lateral or ventral sides. Three broad leaf-like plates (damsel flies) or several short spine-like appendages (dragon fly) at end of abdomen.
(Naiads of Damsel flies and Dragon flies.) Order ODONATA

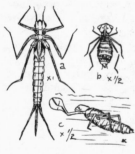

Figure 307

Fig. 307. a, A typical damsel-fly nymph; b, a dragon fly nymph in its early instar; c, a dragon fly nymph with "mask" extended for catching its prey.

These young of dragon flies and damsel flies are abundant in all quiet water courses. They are predaceous in their food habits living largely on other aquatic insects but may even catch small fish. The labium which bears forcep-like parts may be thrust quickly forward a considerable distance as a means of catching prey. If the debris is raked out on the bank from the bottom of a pond, large numbers of these creatures may be secured. If well along they will complete their maturity in captivity.

4b Labium not capable of extension. Long filamentous caudal setae (at end of abdomen). Figs. 308 and 309. 5

5a Gills usually along sides of abdomen; caudal setae usually three, tarsal claws single. (Naiads of May flies). Order EPHEMERIDA

Figure 308

Fig. 308. A Mayfly Nymph.
The life of this growing stage seems to run from four months to two years. Nymphs occur in such great numbers as to make highly valuable food for fish.

5b Gills on underside, for most part on thorax; caudal setae; tarsal claws two. (Naiads of Stoneflies).   **Order PLECOPTERA**

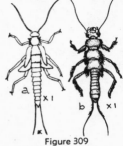

Fig. 309. a, A Stonefly Nymph, *Pteromarcys* sp. with wing sacs about ready to molt into an adult; b, *Aconeura* showing gills attached to the thorax.

These nymphs may be found on top of stones in swift flowing streams. The adults are not often seen except as they fly to lights at night.

Figure 309

6a With jointed thoracic legs. Figs. 311-313. 7

6b Without jointed thoracic legs; wholly legless or with prolegs on abdomen. (Larvae of mosquitos, midges and other aquatic flies.)   **Order DIPTERA**

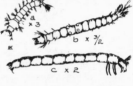

Fig. 310. Some aquatic larvae a, of a mosquito, *Culex* sp.; b, of a Dixamidge; c, of a common midge, *Chironomus* sp.

It will be noted that these larvae have no gills and must come to the surface of the water from time to time for fresh air.

Figure 310

7a Cylindric "worms" usually living in portable cases made of cemented bits of foreign material. (Caddisworms).   **Order TRICHOPTERA**

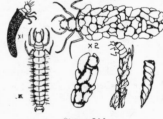

Fig. 311. Several species of Caddisfly larvae and their cases.

These insects live in water and feed on other living things. A few species even build seins in which they catch their prey.

Figure 311

7b Not as in 7a. Figs. 312 and 313. 8

8a Usually without prolegs; terminal spiracles for securing air above water usually present. Lateral filaments, if present, 9 or more pairs.   **Order COLEOPTERA**

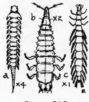

Fig. 312. Larvae of Aquatic Beetles. a, Crawling Water Beetle, Family Haliplidae; b, Water Diving Beetle, *Coptotomus*; c, Whirligig Beetle, *Gyrinus*.

Many water courses resemble our large cities in that they are centers of great populations. One has only to rake out the bottom debris for examination, or to use a fine mesh water net to demonstrate this abundance of aquatic life.

Figure 312

8b Lateral abdominal filaments present, but less than 9 pairs. (Helgramites, etc.). Order NEUROPTERA

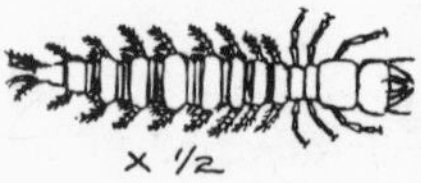

Fig. 313. Helgramite, *Corydalus cornutus.* These "worms" are favorites with fishermen for bait. They abound under rocks in swift flowing streams. Hold a net down stream, turn the rocks and the bait is yours.

x ½

Figure 313

9a Immature forms with wings developing externally. Figs. 314-316. 10

9b Worm-like forms with no wings in evidence. Figs. 317-325 12

10a With chewing mouth parts. (Grasshoppers, Roaches, Crickets, etc.). Order ORTHOPTERA

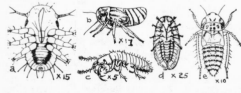

Fig. 314. a, Cockroach nymph, *Periplaneta;* b, young Grasshopper, *Encoptolophus;* c, Field Cricket nymph, *Gryllus assimilis.*

Young Orthoptera are usually very destructive.

Figure 314

·10b With mouth parts united in a beak for sucking. Figs. 315 and 316. 11

11a Sucking beak attached to back part of the head on the under side. (Nymphs of Leaf-hoppers, etc.) Order HOMOPTERA

Fig. 315. Nymphs of Homoptera. a, Peartree Psylla, *Psylla pyricolo;* b, Clover Leafhopper, *Agallia sanguinolenta;* c, Periodical Cicada, *Magicicada septendecim;* d, Maple Scale, *Pulvinaria innum-*

Figure 315

arabilis; e, Destructive Leafhopper, *Athysanus exitiosus,* (U.S.D.A.) These nymphs feed on the sap of plants. Their presence is not readily apparent but their damage is heavy.

11b Sucking beak attached to the front part of the head on the under side. (Nymphs of True Bugs). Order HEMIPTERA

The true bugs form a large and highly important order of very destructive insects. The immature forms often appear in great numbers. Since they feed by a sucking tube contact insecticides are required to kill them.

Figure 316

Fig. 316. Eggs and the five nymph instars of the Common Squash Bug, *Anasa tristis*, (U. S. D. A.).
A careful tour through a garden or wherever plants are growing will reveal many species of this order. Some are beneficial.

12a With prolegs on abdomen. Figs. 317-319. 13

12b Without prolegs. Figs. 320-325. 14

13a With 2 to 5 pair of prolegs, each with many hooks. (Caterpillars). Order LEPIDOPTERA

Figure 317

Fig. 317. a, Yellow-bear Caterpillar, *Diacrisia virginica*; b, Corn-ear or Tomato-fruit Worm, *Heliothis obsoleta*; c, Pupae of the Army Worm, *Cirphis unipuncta*, (U. S. D. A.).
Caterpillars vary greatly in size. Some become great sturdy "worms" four to six inches long and nearly an inch in diameter. The silk-worm caterpillar has been the most useful of all, but synthetic processes are now threatening to push it into a minor place.

13b With eight pairs of prolegs; back of abdomen covered with sharp spines. (Scorpion fly larvae). Order MECOPTERA

Figure 318

Fig. 318. Larva of a Scorpion Fly, *Panorpa*. These larvae are aquatic; they feed on other living forms in the water.

13c With 7 to 9 pairs of prolegs; prolegs do not have hooks. No spines on back. (Sawfly larvae, etc.).   Order HYMENOPTERA (in Part)

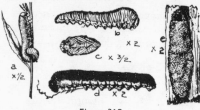

Figure 319

Fig. 319. a, Larva of the American Sawfly, *Cimbex americana;* b and c, Larva and pupa of the Pear Slug, *Eriocampoides limacina;* d and e, Larva and cocoon of the Violet Sawfly, *Emphytus canadensis,* (U. S. D. A.).

14a With jointed thoracic legs. Figs. 320-322. .15

14b Without jointed thoracic legs. Figs. 323-325. 16

15a With mandibles for chewing. (Grubs, etc.).

Order COLEOPTERA (In Part)

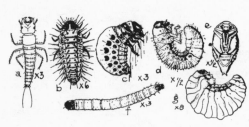

Figure 320

Fig. 320. Some beetle larvae. a, Blister Beetle, *Epicauta vittata;* b, Lady Beetle, *Chilocorus bivulnerus;* c, Colorado Potato Beetle, *Leptinotarsa decimilineata;* d and e, Larva and pupa of a May Beetle, *Phyllophaga* sp.; f, Striped Cucumber Beetle, *Diabrotica vittata;* g, Bean Weevil, *Bruchus* sp., (U.S.D.A.).

15b Feed by sucking through long grooved mandibles. (Ant Lions, Aphis Lions, etc.).

Order NEUROPTERA (In Part)

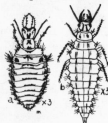

Figure 321

Fig. 321. a, An Ant Lion, *Myrmeleon* sp.; b, An Aphis Lion, *Chrysopa* sp.

The Ant lion is the so-called "Doodle bug" which comes at command. Aphis lions are abundant and very important in helping keep plant lice under control.

15c Mouth parts for chewing. Head with a single ocellus on each side.

Order HYMENOPTERA (In Part)

Figure 322

Fig. 322. *Tremex* sp. Occasional larvae of this order have true legs.

The species here shown is predaceous on a hymenopterous wood borer.

16a With head and mouth parts. Figs. 324 and 325. 17

16b Head poorly developed. (Maggots).   Order DIPTERA (In Part)

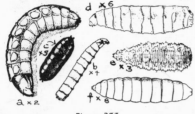

Figure 323

Fig. 323. Some Fly Maggots. a, Robber Fly, *Promachus;* b and c Larva and puparium of the Asparagus Miner, *Agromyza simplex;* d, Cherry Fruit Fly maggot, *Rhagoletis cingulata;* e, a Syrphus Fly, *Syrphus ribesii;* f, Violet Gallfly, *Diplosis violicola,* (U.S.D.A.).

When fly maggots pupate the last larval skin is not shed as with other insects; this resulting stage is then known as a puparium.

17a Very slender worms living on lint, etc. in nests of mammals, cracks in floors, etc. (Flea larvae).   Order SIPHONAPTERA

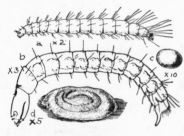

Figure 324

Fig. 324. Flea Larvae; a, European Rat Flea, *Ceratophyllus fasciatus;* b, *Pulex serraticeps;* c and d, Egg and pupa of the Dog Flea, *Ctenocephalus canis,* (U.S.D.A.).

Flea eggs are smooth and are nearly white. They are usually laid while the flea is on the host. The eggs are not fastened in place and soon shatter out of the fur of the host into the nest or elsewhere.

The larvae are very slim white worms about an inch in length. They feed on the waste organic matter in the nest or wherever they chance to grow up.

17b Not as in 17a. Often legless parasites; others legless maggot-like grubs fed by adult directly or depending on stored food.
    Order HYMENOPTERA (In Part)

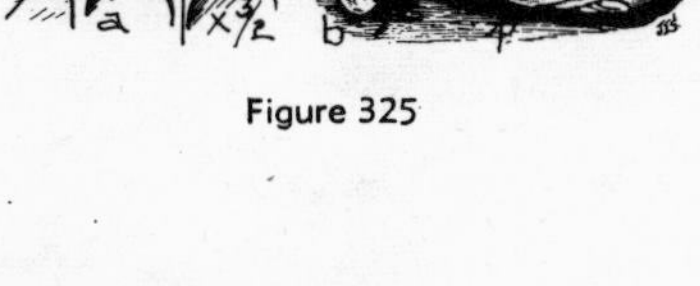

Fig. 325. a, Larvae of the Honey Bee, *Apis melifica;* (Gen. Biol. Sup. House); b, eggs (e), larvae (l) and pupae (p) of an ant, *Iridomyrmex,* (U.S.D.A.).

Many of the Ichneumon and Braconid wasps as well as others live their larval days as parasites within the blood spaces of some insect host. They belong here.

Figure 325

KEY TO THE MORE IMPORTANT ORDERS OF THE CLASS ARACHNIDA

1a Large crab-like marine animals living in shallow water and burrowing in sand. With abdominal appendages and long spike-like tail. But a few species known. (Horseshoe Crabs).

Order XIPHOSURA

Fig. 326. King crab or Horseshoe crab, *Limulus polyphemus*.
These interesting animals burrow in the sand in shallow sea water. Their eggs are laid in holes in the sand along shore.

Figure 326

1b Mostly terrestrial arachnoids having no abdominal appendages. Figs. 327-336. 2

2a Abdomen plainly segmented. Figs. 327-332. 3

2b Abdomen not segmented. Figs. 333-336. 8

3a With a long, segmented, tail-like structure. Figs. 327 and 328....4

3b Without long tail-like structure. Figs. 329-332. 5

4a Last segment of tail enlarged and bearing a poisonous sting. (The Scorpions).   Order SCORPIONIDA

Fig. 327. A Scorpion, *Anuroctonus*.
Scorpions are well known for their recklessness in stinging and the painfulness of it. A friend who has had considerable experience recommends the prompt application of ice to the wound. He claims the pain will soon be relieved. We have not sought an occasion to try it, so offer it only for what it may be worth.

x ⅔

Figure 327

4b Tail, a thread-like filament; (members of one family, Tarantilidae (Fig. 332) have no tail). Order PEDIPALPI

Figure 328

Fig. 328. A Whip Scorpion, *Mastigoproctus*.

Whip scorpions have no sting and are not poisonous. They attain a length of several inches and are gruesome in appearance.

5a Head bearing three pairs of appendages, chelicera, pedipalps and legs. Distinctly separated from the thorax which has 3 segments, each bearing a pair of legs. Order SOLPUGIDA

Figure 329

Fig. 329. *Eremobates*.

These animals are most frequent in tropical deserts. They are nocturnal in habit and are not poisonous. A few species are found in the United States.

5b Head and thorax fused into one structure. Figs. 330-332. 6

6a Pedipalps long and tipped with large pincer-like structures. Order PSEUDOSCORPIONIDA

Figure 330

Fig. 330. *Apocheiridium*.

These strange little creatures never fail to attract attention. The long-pincer-like pedipalps are carried so solemnly as to give a grotesque appearance. One rather common species is found on old books, etc.

6b Not as in 6a. Figs. 331 and 332. 7

7a Body comparatively small and egg shaped. Legs very long and slender. (Grand-Daddy-Longlegs). **Order PHALANGIDA**

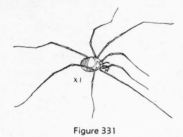

Figure 331

Fig. 331. *Phalangium.*
These animals besides being supposed to "point the direction of the cows" for country children have some economic importance in damaging fruit.

7b Body proportionately larger. Cephalothorax broader than abdomen. **Order PEDIPALPI (In Part)**

Figure 332

Fig. 332. *Tarantula whitei;* South West United States.

8a Aquatic animals. Figs. 335 and 336. 10

8b Living on land. Figs. 333 and 334. 9

9a Cephalothorax distinctly separated from abdomen. (Spiders). **Order ARANEIDA**

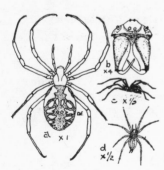

Figure 333

Fig. 333. a, The Garden Spider, *Argiope;* b,. head of garden spider showing eyes and mandibles; c, Black Widow Spider, *Latrodectus mactans;* d, Grass Spider, *Agelena naevia.*

To this order belong more than 10,000 species of spiders. Since their food consists largely of insects they are highly beneficial. Spiders are equipped with poison glands but since only a few of them can bite through our skin the danger is not at all great. The Black Widow is dangerous; few others need to be given serious consideration.

9b Cephalothorax and abdomen fused into one part. (Mites, Ticks).
Order ACARINA

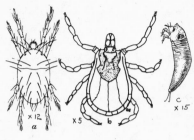

Fig. 334. Common "Red Spider", *Tetranychus;* b, Spotted Fever Tick, *Dermacentor venustus;* c, Rust Mite, *Phytoptus.* Some mites are plant feeders; others suck blood from animals. The ticks are feared because of the diseases they transmit.

Figure 334

Mites are often serious pests of birds and mammals. Unlike lice, they torment their hosts only at night and hide by day in the nest or roosts of their victims.

Ticks are bad by reputation and fact in transmitting some very dangerous diseases. Some mites are highly destructive to plants; others feed on birds.

10a With four pairs of short legs. Microscopic forms. (Water Bears).
Order TARDIGRADA

Figure 335

Fig. 335. A Water Bear, *Echiniscus* sp.
These tiny aquatic animals are poorly known and apparently of little consequence, except for their scientific interest. They are both fresh water and marine.

10b With 7 pairs of long slender appendages. Marine. (Sea Spiders).
Order PYCNOGONIDA

Figure 336

Fig. 336. *Nymphon hispidum.*
The four pairs of legs and three pairs of anterior appendages constitute the conspicuous parts of these rather small animals. They are found living amid the marine algae. The larvae are worm-like.

KEY TO THE SUBPHYLA AND CLASSES OF THE PHYLUM CHORDATA

1a Animals having a vertebral column (chain of bones) on dorsal side. Brain at anterior end of nerve cord. (The Vertebrates). Figs. 340-421. 4
Subphylum, VERTEBRATA (Craniata)

1b Without vertebral column. Animals of but little importance and poorly known except by biologists. Figs. 337-339. 2

CHORDATES

2a With continuous rod of cartilage (Notochord) in the back of the elongated animal to stiffen it. No skull, jaws or paired appendages. Marine. (Amphioxus, The Lancelet).

Subphylum, CEPHALOCHORDA
Order CIRROSTOMI

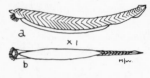

Figure 337

Fig. 337. Amphioxus, *Branchiostoma lanceolatus;* a, side view; b, ventral view. About 30 species, widely distributed.

These simple little creatures have no head, no eyes, no brain, but even at that are not much worse off than those who have these organs and fail to use them.

2b Notochord not present in adult, or at most but poorly developed. Figs. 338 and 339. 3

3a Adult worm-like with three body parts — (a) proboscis; (b) collar; (c) trunk; Marine. (Size 1 inch to 4 ft.)

Subphylum, ENTEROPNEUSTA
Order BALANOGLOSSIDA

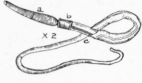

Figure 338

Fig. 338. *Dolichoglossus,* (Courtesy General Biological Supply House).

If it were not for the notochord and gill slits these animals would pass for worms. They are plainly Chordates but not very good ones.

3b Adult rounded or elongated; attached animals. Sac-like covering with two large openings. Larva shaped like a tadpole with notochord in the tail. (The Sea Squirts or Sea Peaches.)

Subphylum, TUNICATA

Figure 339

Fig. 339. a, *Clavellina,* with lateral bud; b, a colony of *Botryllus violaceus.*

It was not until the larva was studied that the Tunicates were even suspected of being Chordates.

4a Aquatic vertebrates with fins for locomotion. (Cold blooded). Figs. 340-368
(If fins belong to larval stage only (Figs. 369d and 370d) go to Amphibia p. 131 instead). "The Fishes" (Including Four Classes) p. 117

4b Aquatic or land forms moving by aid of legs or wings, (a few without appendages). Figs. 369-421. 5

120

5a Cold blooded vertebrates; naked skin or covered with scales.
Figs. 369-374. 6

5b Warm blooded vertebrates; with covering of feathers or of hair.
Figs. 375-421. 7

6a Naked skin (a few have scales). If fins are present they are without
rays. Usually hatch as tadpoles from small shell-less eggs.
(The Frogs, Toads, Salamanders, etc.). Figs. 369 and 370.
Class AMPHIBIA p. 131

6b Covered with scales or bony plates. Eggs large and covered with
tough membrane or shell; or young born alive. (Snakes, Turtles,
Lizards, etc.). Figs. 371-374.   Class REPTILIA p. 132

7a Covered with feathers; young hatch from large hard-shelled eggs.
Usually with two legs and a pair of wings. (The Birds).
Figs. 375-404.   Class AVES p. 133

7b Covered in whole or in part with hair. Young fed on milk secreted
by female. (The Mammals). Figs. 405-421.
Class MAMMALIA p. 145

KEY TO THE CLASSES AND MORE IMPORTANT ORDERS OF THE FISHES

1a Naked eel-shaped vertebrates with no jaws or paired fins and with
a single median nostril. (Skeleton of cartilage.)
Figs. 340 and 341. 2
Class CYCLOSTOMATA

1b With jaws. Figs. 342 and 368. 3

2a Without eyes; Gill opening (a) remote from head. Marine.
(The Hagfishes).   Order MYXINOIDAE

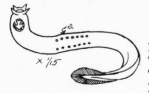

Figure 340

Fig. 340. *Myxine glutinosa.*
They eat their way into the flesh of fishes.
This species is found in deep water off the
New England and Newfoundland coast.

2b With eyes; gill openings near head. Both marine and fresh water. (The Lamprey Eels). **Order PETROMYZONTIA**

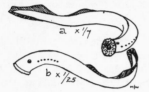

Figure 341

Fig. 341. a, Silvery Lamprey, *Ichthyomyzon concolor;* b, Great Sea Lamprey, *Petromyzon marinus.*
The eggs of some species are laid at the head waters of small streams.

3a Skeleton cartilaginous. Tail heterocercal (Fig. 341½). Gills not free. Eggs few and large. Marine. Figs. 342-345. 4

Figure 341½
Heterocercal Tail

3b Skeleton of bone, gills free; eggs small and very numerous. Both marine and fresh water. (True Fishes). Figs. 346-368. 7

Class PISCES

4a Outer gill opening single with 4 gill slits inside. (The Chimeras).

Class HOLOCEPHALI
Order CHIMAEROIDEI

Figure 342

Fig. 342. Chimera, *Psychichthys;* Deep water marine fishes.
A lot of fancy has been mixed with some facts about this group. They are uncommon.

4b Outer gill slits, 5 to 7 pairs (Fig. 344, g) (Sharks and Rays). Figs. 343-345. 5

Class ELASMOBRANCHII

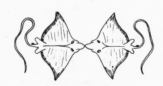

KEY TO THE ORDERS OF THE CLASS ELASMOBRANCHII

5a Flattened in form with the gill openings (o) on under side. Often with long whip-like tails. (The Sawfishes, Skates and Rays.)

Order BATOIDEI

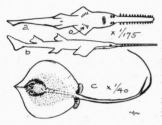

Figure 343

Fig. 343. The Sawfish, *Pristis pectinatus;* a, ventral view; b, side view; c, The Sting Ray, *Trygon sabina.*
The Sea-devils are the largest of all the rays. They may have a width of over 20 feet and a weight of 1250 pounds.

5b Elongate and rather narrow in form with gill slits on sides. Figs. 344 and 345. 6

6a With anal fin (a); scales minute. (The True Sharks).

Order EUSELACHII

Figure 344

Fig. 344. Tiger Mackerel Shark, *Isurus tigris.* To this order belong the large voracious sharks. The Man-eater Shark which attains a length of 35 feet belongs here. Fossil remains of a species 150 feet long have been found.

6b Without anal fin. (The Dogfishes, etc.).   **Order CYCLOSPONDYLI**

Figure 345

Fig. 345. Dogfish Shark, Grayfish, *Squalus acanthias.*
Common in Atlantic ocean north of Cuba.

KEY TO THE MORE COMMON ORDERS OF THE CLASS PISCES

7a With both lungs and gills for respiration. Rudimentary legs and molar teeth. (The Lung-fishes). Order DIPNOI

Figure 346

Fig. 346. a, Australian Lung-Fish, *Ceratodus forsteri*; b, African Mudfish, *Protopterus annectens*.

This order is represented by five known species. They are intermediate between the fishes and the Amphibia. When the water courses in which they live become stagnant or dry up, they use their lungs instead of the gills which function while in water.

7b Without lungs. Fins with no central axis; supported by fin rays. Figs. 348-368. 8

8a Skeleton cartilaginous or bony. Long cylindrical fish with protruding snout or with spines on nose. Figs. 348-351. 9

8b Skeleton bony. Fishes of various forms. Tail usually homoceral (a); Scales cycloid (b) or ctenoid (c) or wanting. (The True Bony Fishes.) Figs. 352-368. 12
Super–order, TELEOSTEI

Figure 347

9a Body without scales. Snout a long paddle-like structure. (The Paddle Fish.) Order SELACHOSTOMI

Figure 348

Fig. 348. Spoonbill, Duck-billed Cat, *Polyodon spatula*; a, side view; b, ventral view. Common in Mississippi River system. It occasionally weight up to 200 pounds and is prized as a food fish.

9b Not as is 9a. Figs. 349-351. 10

10a Large, elongate fish with five longitudinal rows of keeled bony plates. (The Sturgeons.) Order **GLANIOSTOMI**

Figure 349

Fig. 349. River Sturgeon. *Acipenser fulvescens.*
A very important food fish; the eggs are particularly in demand. Some twenty living species of Sturgeons are known.

10b Not as in 10a. Figs. 350 and 351. 11

11a Scales ganoid (a). Snout long and terminal and set with stout teeth. (Gars). Order **GINGLYMODI**

Figure 350

Fig. 350. The Longnosed Gar Pike, *Lepidosteus osseus.*
The Gars are generally hated by fishermen. They are likely not as bad as usually supposed.

11b Scales cycloid (b). Mouth broad, terminal and jaws set with teeth. (The Bowfins or Dogfish). Order **HALECOMORPHI**

Figure 351

Fig. 351. Dogfish, *Amia calva.*
This species is the sole representative of its order. It comes to the surface for air to fill a lung sack and can live actively in stagnant water. It is an enemy of all living things within its reach.

12a Body without scales (a few species with very small scales). Figs. 352-354. 13

12b Body in whole or in part covered with scales. Figs. 355-368....15

13a Head broad and flattened; barbels (a) around mouth; defensive spines in dorsal and pectoral fins. (The Catfishes.)
Order **NEMATOGNATHI**

Figure 352

Fig. 352. Channel Cat, *Ictalurus punctatus.*
In all there are about 1000 species of known catfish. The Mississippi Cat is the largest in our region. It attains a weight of 100 pounds or more.

13b Long slender snake-like. No central fins. Figs. 353 and 354....14

14a With pectoral fins. Gill openings, wide slits (a). (The Eels.)
Order ENCHELYCEPHALI

Figure 353

Fig. 353. American Eel, *Anguilla bostoniensis*.
This valuable food fish is highly interesting in its migration. When sexually mature the adults descend the rivers and go to the Atlantic ocean to spawn and die.

14b No pectoral fins. Gill openings small round pores. (The Morays.)
Order COLOCEPHALI

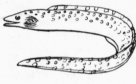

Figure 354

Fig. 354. Spotted Moray, *Gymnothorax moringa*.
This is a large order but not very well known. Some species are several feet in length and equipped with long sharp teeth. They coil and strike like snakes, and bite savagely. Several species are used for food. They are often brilliantly colored. They are widely distributed in marine waters.

15a Rather small marine fishes with bony armor. Mouth tubular; gills tufted. (Sea Horses and Pipe Fish.)
Order LOPHOBRANCHII

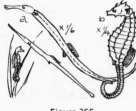

Figure 355

Fig. 355. a, Pipefish, *Syngnathus*; b, Sea Horse, *Hippocampus*.
Pipe fish feed by inserting their slim heads into the openings of sponges and corals. The Sea Horses always swim in a vertical position. The eggs are deposited in the brood pouch of the male and retained there until hatched.

15b Not as in 15a. Figs. 356-368. 16

16a Small fresh water fish with from 2 to 15 prominent spines on the back. Usually build nests. (The Sticklebacks).

Order HEMIBRANCHII

Fig. 356. Two-Spined Stickleback, *Gladiunculus wheatlandi,* showing nest.
There are several species of Sticklebacks in our country. The number of dorsal spines is one character for distinguishing them.

Figure 356

16b Not as in 16a. Figs. 357-368. 17

17a Bottom feeding marine fish with enormous mouth and broad flattened body. (The Anglers, Bat Fishes and Frog Fishes).

Order PEDICULATI

Fig. 357. a, Bat Fish, *Ogcocephalus;* b, Angler, Fishing Frog, *Lophius.*
The fish in this group partly cover themselves with sand. Many species have a lure of some sort to attract their prey.

Figure 357

17b Not as in 17a. Figs. 358-368. 18

18a Medium sized torpedo shaped marine fish with conspicuous sucking disk on top of head. (The Remoras).

Order DISCOCEPHALI

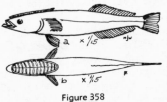

Fig. 358. *Echeneis naucrates;* a, side view; b, dorsal view.
The Remoras cling to sharks and other large fish by means of their sucking disk. They are in no way parasitic but just enjoy "hitch-hiking".

Figure 358

18b Without sucking disk on top of head. Figs. 359-368. 19

19a Marine fish with greatly enlarged pectoral fins for flying or gliding. (The "Flying" Gurnard of the Atlantic Coast does not belong here.) (Flying Fish). **Order SYNENTOGNATHI**

Figure 359

Fig. 359. *Exonautes.*
These necessary adjuncts to every successful ocean voyage should perhaps be better called "gliding fish" as it seems their large pectoral fins are held stationary during flight.

19b Not able to glide by means of large pectoral fins. Figs. 360-368 . . . . **20**

20a Flat, oval, marine, with distorted mouth and both eyes on same side. Swim with a flying-rug effect. (The Flat Fishes, Halibuts, Flounders, Soles, etc.). **Order HETEROSOMATA**

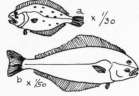
Figure 360

Fig. 360. a, Summer Flounder, *Paralichthys dentatus;* b, Halibut, *Hippoglossus hippoglossus.*
Many valuable food fish fall in this order. The Halibut is the largest member and of the greatest commercial importance. It is known to reach a length of eight feet and to weigh 600 pounds.

20b Not as in 20a. Figs. 361-368. . . . . **21**

21a Pelvic fins (second set of paired fins) arising from abdomen. No fins with spiny rays. Figs. 365-368. . . . . **24**

21b Pelvic fins as in 21a, but with 2 or 3 spiny rays in dorsal and anal fins. (The Carp and Gold Fish.) **Order EVENTOGNATHI (In Part)**

Figure 361

Fig. 361. a, Common Goldfish; b, "Japanese Fantail"; c, "Comet" Goldfish; *Carassius auratus.*
Neither gold fish or carp are natives of America. Gold fish were first domesticated in China. There are many forms but all are the same species.

21c Pelvic fins usually arising near head and close to pectoral fins (a, Fig. 362). Pelvic fins usually with spiny ray and five soft ones. Front rays of dorsal and pectoral fins usually spiny. Figs. 362-364. 22

22a Adipose fin (fleshy fin (f) back of dorsal fin) present. (The Trout Perches.)   Order SALMOPERCAE

Fig. 362. Sand Roller, *Percopsis omiscomaycus.*
This species is found in the Great Lakes, Lake Okoboji and in a number of the rivers of the eastern and middle United States.

Figure 362

22b Without adipose (fleshy) fin. Figs. 363 and 364. 23

23a With bony plate on cheek. Body not uniformly scaled. (The Mailed-Cheek Fishes.)   Order CATAPHRACTI

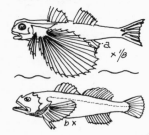

Fig. 363. a, Flying Gurnard, *Dactylopterus volitans;* b, *Myoxocephalus niger.*
The Flying Gurnards are highly colorful. They are found in the warmer seas. Their ability in flight is quite limited. The Sea Robin is common off our Atlantic coast.

Figure 363

23b Without bony plate on cheek. Body uniformly scaled. (The Spiny-rayed Fishes.)   Order ACANTHOPTERI

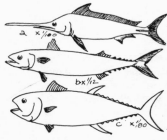

Fig. 364. a, Sword Fish, *Xiphias gladius;* b, Common Mackerel, *Scomber scombrus;* c, Tuna, *Thunnus thynnus.*
The Sword Fish is found living its solitary life in all warm seas. Its unprovoked and violent attacks upon boats and other large objects that cross its path are hard to explain. It is prized for food.

Figure 364

24a Head not scaly. Figs. 365 and 366. 25

24b Head more or less covered with scales. Figs. 367 and 368......26

25a With 6 or more branchiostegal rays. (Bony rays stiffening the membrane immediately behind the gill covers.) (Salmon, Trout,
Order ISOSPONDYLI

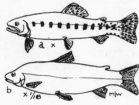

Figure 365

Fig. 365. a, Golden Trout, *Salmo roosevelti;* b, White Fish, *Coregonus clupeaformis.*
Here belong some of our very best food and game fishes. Many live in fresh water; others are marine. The order is a large one.

25b With only 3 branchiostegal rays. (Suckers, Minnows, etc.).
Order EVENTOGNATHI (In Part)

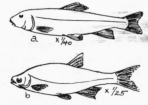

Figure 366

Fig. 366. a, Common Sucker, *Catastomas commersoni;* b, Golden Shiner, *Abramis crysoleucas.*
Some sixty species of suckers are known. They are widely distributed in our inland streams but are rather inferior as food fish.

26a Side margin of upper jaw formed by the maxillaries. Small and large fish. (Mud Minnows, Pikes, etc.).
Order HAPLOMI

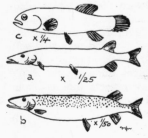

Figure 367

Fig. 367. a, Great Northern Pike, *Esox lusius;* b Muskallunge, *Esox masquinongy;* c, Eastern Mud Minnow, *Umbra pygmaea.*
The Pike and Muskallunge are noble game fish. The latter reaches a length of six feet and may weigh 80 pounds.

26b Premaxillaries forming side margins of upper jaw. Small fish. (Killifish, Top Minnows, Cave Fish, etc.). Order CYPRINODONTES

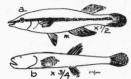

Fig. 368. a, Top Minnow, *Zygonectes notatus*; b, Lesser Blind Fish, *Typhlichthys subterraneus*. Just how or why cave fish became blind and how many centuries it has taken them to reach this condition arouses one's interest.

Figure 368

KEY TO THE IMPORTANT ORDERS OF THE CLASS AMPHIBIA

1a Body long; with a tail throughout life. Hind limbs if present not much enlarged. (Salamanders, Newts, Sirens, Mud Puppies, etc.). In Tadpoles the body tapers gradually into the tail.

Order CAUDATA

Figure 369

Fig. 369. a, Mud Eel or Siren, *Siren lacertina*; b, Mud Puppy, *Necturus maculatus*; c, Spotted Salamander, *Amblystoma punctatum*; d, Salamander tadpole.

The Giant Salamander of Japan which attains a length of three feet is the largest member of its order. Salamanders are often mistaken for lizards but may be readily distinguished by having no scales. The order is highly interesting but of comparatively little economic importance.

1b Adult short and tailless; young (tadpole) with a long tail which is absorbed at maturity. Hind limbs enlarged. In tadpoles the body tapers abruptly into the tail. (Frogs and Toads).

Order SALIENTIA

Figure 370

Fig. 370. a, Bull Frog, *Rana catesbeiana*; b, Common Toad, *Bufo* sp.; c, Tree Frog, *Hyla versicolor*; d, Frog Tadpole.

Toads and frogs lay their eggs in water in early spring. They are surrounded by a gelatinous covering. Frog eggs are separate from each other and roughly resemble tapioca that has been soaked. Toad eggs are laid in long strings in a tangled mass.

KEY TO THE MORE COMMON ORDERS OF
THE CLASS REPTILIA

1a Jaws without teeth. Body usually in a shell. (Turtles, Terrapins, Tortoises.)　　　　　　　　　　　　　　　　Order TESTUDINATA

Figure 371

Fig. 371. a, Common Soft Shelled Tortoise, *Amydia spinifera*; b, Box Terrapin, *Terrapene*; c, Green Turtle, *Chelonia mydas*; d, Common Snapping Tortoise, *Chelydra serpentina*.

If one wishes to speak with precision he will call all fresh water forms of this order "Terrapins"; those that live principally on land "Tortoises" and reserve the term "Turtles" for marine species.

1b Jaws with teeth. Figs. 372-374. 2

2a Teeth in sockets; anus a longitudinal slit. (Crocodiles and Alligators.)　　　　　　　　　　　　　　　　Order CROCODILIA

Figure 372

Fig. 372. a, American Alligator, *Alligator mississippiensis*; b, a Crocodile, *Crocodylus*.

There are some old-world alligators and likewise some new-world crocodiles, popular opinion to the contrary not-withstanding. The shape of the head makes the determining character.

2b Teeth not in sockets; anal opening a cross slit. Figs. 373 and 374. 3

3a With two pairs of legs (rarely none) eyelids and external ear-opening with drum usually present. (Lizards, Skinks, Gecko, Iguanas, Glass Snakes, etc.). Order LACERTILIA

Fig. 373. a, Iguana, *Iguana tuberculata;* b, Glass "Snake", *Ophisaurus ventralis;* c, Skink, *Eumeces skiltonianus;* d, Collared Lizard, *Crotaphytus collaris.* Don't catch your lizards by the tail if you want good specimens. Their tails are very brittle.

Figure 373

3b Without legs, eyelids or external ear-openings. Much elongated. (Snakes). Order SERPENTES

Fig. 374. a, Common Rattlesnake, *Crotalus horridus;* b, Blue Racer, *Coluber constrictor flaviventris;* c, Puff Adder or Spreading Viper, *Heterodon contortrix.*

Figure 374

Rattlesnakes, of which there are several species, are all dangerous. Blue Racers and Spreading Vipers are not poisonous; the latter will not even bite and makes an interesting pet.

KEY TO THE MORE COMMON ORDERS OF LIVING BIRDS (AVES)

1a Flightless birds (wings too small or weak to sustain the bird in prolonged flight). Usually large stockily-built birds. Figs. 375-379. 2

1b Birds not as in 1a. Figs. 381-404. 6

133

2a Large birds with but two toes on each foot. Natives of Africa. (The Ostriches.) Order STRUTHIONIFORMES

Figure 375

Fig. 375. Ostrich, *Struthio camelus*.
The Ostrich is a native of Africa. For a sentence of interest, another (likely futile) effort will be made to kill the yarn of the ostrich burying its head in the sand. It is a "fairy story" without foundation.
There is but the one species. It is our largest living bird. An ostrich can outrun a horse.

2b With more than two toes. Figs. 376-379. 3

3a Feet webbed. Birds spending much time in the water. Stand erect when on land. (The Penguins.) Order SPHENISCIFORMES

Figure 376

Fig. 376. A Penguin.
These interesting birds are confined to the southern hemisphere. They spend much of the time in water for they are excellent swimmers. The Emperor Penguin, largest of all, stands more than three feet high.

3b Feet not webbed. Figs. 377-379. 4

4a Wingless and tailless. About the size of a chicken. Feathers somewhat hair-like. (Kiwis). Order APTERYGIFORMES·

Figure 377

Fig. 377. The Kiwi, *Apteryx australis*.
A native of New Zealand, the Kiwi or Apteryx is threatened with extinction. They nest in a hole in the ground and feed on worms for which they probe in the mud with their long bill.

4b Not as in 4a. Figs. 378 and 379. 5

5a Head and neck covered with feathers. Natives of South America. (The Rheas). Order RHEIFORMES

Figure 378

Fig. 378. *Rhea americana.*
These large "South American Ostriches" have long been valuable game birds for the Indians of their region. Rheas are easily tamed. They stand some five feet in height, and are bluish-gray in color. They have longer wings than the other ostrich-like birds.

5b Head and neck without feathers. Natives of Australia and New Guinea. (Cassowaries and Emus.) Order CASUARIIFORMES

Figure 379

Fig. 379. Cassowary, *Casuarius galeatus.*
The head decorations are highly colored but the bird is possessed of an evil temper. It kicks with great force and rapidity. The wing feathers are round black shafts not unlike porcupine quills.
The Emu attains a height of over five feet but seems to be quite inoffensive. In contrast to the white eggs of the other flightless birds, the Emu lays six or seven dark green eggs.

6a Water birds. With feet webbed for swimming; or with long legs for wading. Figs. 380-393. 7

6b Land birds. Feet not webbed. Legs not unusually long. Figs. 394-404. 17

7a Web of foot extending to back toe. Large birds, two feet or more in length. (Pelicans, Cormorants, Snake birds, Gannets, etc.).

Order PELICANIFORMES

Figure 380

Figure 381

Fig. 381. a, White Pelican, *Pelecanus erythrorhynchos;* b, Water Turkey, *Anhinga anhinga.*
Pelicans are friendly birds but their enormous appetite for fresh fish makes one an expensive pet. The Water Turkey or Snake Bird pursues and catches fish under water.

7b Hind toe free or wanting; not attached to others by the web. Figs. 382-393....8

Figure 382

8a Wings practically devoid of feathers and used only for swimming. (The Penguins.) Fig. 376.   Order SPHENISCIFORMES

8b Not as in 8a. Figs. 383-393. 9

9a Feet webbed or lobed for swimming or diving. Legs fairly short. Figs. 383-388. 10

9b Wading birds. Legs usually long. Feet seldom webbed. Figs. 389-393. 15

10a Legs inserted well behind the middle of the body, requiring the bird to stand somewhat erect when on land. Strong divers. Figs. 383-385. 11

10b Legs not inserted much behind the middle of the body; body when standing, nearly horizontal. Figs. 386-388.............13

11a Without tail feathers. Front toes lobed. Claws broad, flat and rounded. Head held erect when swimming. (The Grebes.)
Order COLYMBIFORMES

Figure 383

Fig. 383. Horned Grebe, *Colymbus auritus.*
Grebes rely on their ability in diving and swimming and fly but little except during their migration. The food consists largely of fish which they pursue under water.

11b With short tail feathers. Figs. 384 and 385. 12

12a Hind toe present making 4 in all. Large birds with long pointed bill. (The Loons.) **Order GAVIIFORMES**

Figure 384

Fig. 384. A Loon, *Gavia immer.*
Found in lakes of the north. Unexcelled in diving and swimming. Its peculiar call is responsible for the remark "crazier than a loon".
Its colors are black and white which make it very trim in appearance. It is an expert fishes. It cannot take off in flight except when in water.

12b Hind toe absent. Three toes in all. (Auks, Puffins, Murres, etc.).
Order CHARADRIIFORMES (In Part)

Figure 385

Fig. 385. a, Murre, *Uria troille;* b, Razor-Billed Auk, *Alca torda;* c, Puffin or Sea Parrot, *Fratercula arctica.*
These birds are all excellent swimmers. They nest in colonies on rocky coasts. They fly well but must have water on which to get started or plunge from some height.

137

13a Bill with inner plate-like part; bill broad, flattened or narrow with toothed edges. Tail well developed. (Ducks, Geese, Swans.)
Order **ANSERIFORMES**

Fig. 386. a, A Duck; b, A Swan, *Cygnus columbianus*; c, Canada Goose, *Branta canadensis*.

Flocks of these birds are familiar sights during the migratory seasons. They are favorites with hunters and are protected by both state and federal regulations.

Figure 386

The wild ducks separate themselves rather naturally into three groups. The Mergansers or Saw-bills are fish eating ducks and may be distinguished by their cylindrical bills. They pursue and catch their prey under water.

The River and Pond Ducks are poor divers. They live in small companies and are often seen "tipping up" when feeding. The Mallard, the Teals, the Pintail and the Wood Duck are favorites. All of these will live and nest happily in semi-domestication if given a protected water course and a little feed.

The Bay or Diving Ducks have a lobe on the hind toe. Some of them are said to descend 150 feet or more into the water.

13b Bill not as in 13a. Figs. 387 and 388. 14

14a Nostrils enclosed in an arched tube (a). Bill hooked. (Albatrosses, Petrels, Sheerwaters.)
Order **PROCELLARIIFORMES**

Fig. 387. Wandering Albatross, *Diomedea exulans*.
Like most of the other albatrosses this bird belongs to the Southern hemisphere. It is an artistic expert both in the air and on the waves. Large specimens have a 12 foot spread of wings.

Figure 387

14b Nostrils not tubular. Long wings. Sturdy fliers. (Gulls, Terns, etc.). **Order CHARADRIIFORMES (In Part)**

Fig. 388. a, A Gull, *Larus* sp.; b, A Tern, *Sterna* sp.
Gulls are on the average larger and bulkier than terns; their bills are slightly hooked. Terns have long, slim, sharp pointed bills. Both are tireless fliers.

Figure 388

15a Longlegged, red or pink and white birds; bill bent downward; three front toes, webbed. (Flamingoes.) **Order CICONIIFORMES (In Part)**

Fig. 389. Flamingo, *Phoenicopterus ruber.*
Eight species of flamingoes are known. All are tropical. They are gregarious in their nesting and feeding.
They construct a stump-like pillar of mud on which to lay their two eggs and hatch their downy young. Dr. Chapman reports seeing 2,000 of these nests in one group on a mud flat in the Bahamas.

Figure 389

15b Longlegged wading birds. Toes four, but slightly webbed if at all; hind toe strong and usually on same level with front ones. Area between eye and bill (lores) naked. (Herons, Bitterns, Storks, Ibeses, Spoonbills.) **Order CICONIIFORMES (In Part)**

Fig. 390. a, Roseate Spoonbill, *Ajaia ajaja;* American Bittern, *Botaurus lentiginosus;* c, Great Blue Heron, *Ardea herodias.*
Our Great Blue Heron is a majestic bird and common enough that all who have opportunity to visit our inland lakes or streams may see and enjoy it.

Figure 390

Figure 391

15c Not as in 15a or 15b. Hind toe small or absent. Lores feathered or with bristles. The Rails, some quite small, as well as some other birds, belong here. Figs. 391-393. 16

16a Longlegged, usually slender billed shore birds. (Usually smaller birds, never over 2 ft. long). Hind toe if present higher than others. (Snipes, Sandpipers, Plovers, etc.).

Order CHARADRIIFORMES (In Part)

Figure 392

Fig. 392. a, American Woodcock, *Philohela minor*; b, A Sandpiper. These shore birds are regarded highly as game; nature lovers prefer to hunt with field glasses and a camera and would rather let them live.

16b Toes, four without web. (Coots have lobes on toes). Neck extended in flight. Coots and Gallinules belonging here have forehead bare. (Cranes, Courlans, Rails, Gallinules, Coots, etc.).

Order GRUIFORMES

Figure 393

Fig. 393. a, Whooping Crane, *Grus americana*; b, Coot, *Fulica americana*. Rails are almost chicken-like in their build and habits. The lobes on the toes of the Coot make it an excellent swimmer and at the same time permit it to run over soft mud without sinking in.

17a Bill strongly hooked at tip; cere (fleshy or membranous growth) at base of bill. Figs. 394-396. 18

17b Bill without strong hook and cere. Figs. 397-404. 20

18a Toes permanently two in front and two behind. Lower bill scoop shaped. Fruit eaters. Usually brilliant colors. (Parrots, Cockatoos, Paroquets, etc.). Order PSITTACIFORMES

Figure 394

Fig. 394. a, Pink Cockatoo, *Cacatua leadbeateri*; b, Paroquets, Love Birds, *Psittacula* sp.

Members of this order are known for their long life and for their intelligence. "Love birds" whether of this order or of the order Primates seem to belong in pairs.

18b Toes three in front and one behind; the outer toe often reversible. Claws strong, sharp and curved. Figs. 395 and 396.............19

19a Eyes at front of head and surrounded by feathered disks. Plumage fluffy. (Owls). Order STRIGIFORMES

Figure 395

Fig. 395. Screech Owl, *Otus asio*, (U. S. D. A.).

Birds, like folks, are neither wholly bad or entirely good. Most species of owls offer more help to man than annoyance and are worthy of protection. The owls soft plumage make them the very quiet fliers.

19b Eyes at sides of head, not surrounded by feathered disk. Plumage compact. (Vultures, Eagles, Hawks, etc.).

Order FALCONIFORMES

Figure 396

Fig. 396. a, Turkey Buzzard, *Cathartes aura;* b, Marsh Hawk, *Circus hudsonius.*
Many hawks are highly useful in destroying harmful rodents. The Turkey Vulture's value as a scavenger has long been recognized.

20a Hind toe short and noticeably elevated above the others. Terrestrial scratching birds with short stout bill, and short wings. (Pheasants, Turkeys, Quails, Grouse, etc.).

Order GALLIFORMES

Figure 397

Fig. 397. Bob White or Quail, *Colinus virginianus,* (U. S. D. A.). Many of the members of this order are semi-domesticated birds. We pay to have them raised and released and then pay again for the privilege of shooting them.

20b Hind toe on level with others or nearly so. Figs. 398-404. 21

21a Bill deeply grooved. Nostril openings covered with a soft fleshy membrane (cere) (c). (Doves and Pigeons).

Order COLUMBIFORMES

Figure 398

Fig. 398. Mourning Dove, *Zenaidura macroura.*
The mention of this order always brings to mind the Passenger Pigeon whose great flocks once darkened the sky, but which is now extinct.

21b Nostrils not as in 21a. Figs. 399-404. 22

22a Climbing birds with heavy chisel-like bills and stiff tail feathers for propping; toes, two in front and two behind, (rarely two in front and one behind). Often marked with red on the head, especially the males. Nostrils covered with feathers. (Woodpeckers.) Order PICIFORMES

Fig. 399. Hairy Woodpecker, *Dryobates villosus*.
Woodpeckers are scattered world wide. They are volunteer tree inspectors and do a valuable service in removing wood boring insects. Several species of woodpeckers as well as some other birds come readily to offerings of suet during the winter. The feed may be placed on a tree or post within a few feet of a window and children as well as grown-ups will get many pleasant moments watching these little friends at close range.

Figure 399

22b Not as in 22a. Figs. 400-404. 23

23a Bill very short, mouth wide and surrounded by heavy bristles. Wings long and pointed. Plumage, fluffy. (Whip-poor-wills, Nighthawks, etc.). Order CAPRIMULGIFORMES

Fig. 400. The Nighthawk, *Chordeiles minor*. (R. L. Sim). This birds seems to belong to the city. Its eggs are laid on the flat roofs of buildings and the young reared there. Their color pattern blends with unusal fidelity with its surroundings. In the country the eggs are laid on lichen covered rocks. They build no nests.

Figure 400

23b Feathers compact; bill very long and slender, usually tiny swift flying birds of brilliant irridescent plumage; (The Humming Birds, Fig. 401) or bill very short, mouth wide, without bristles surrounding the mouth. (The Swifts).   Order MICROPODIFORMES

Figure 401

Fig. 401. Ruby-throated Hummingbird, (U. S. D. A.).

This tiny living jewel is an inspiration to every one. The Western Hemisphere has many humming birds but this is the only one that visits the eastern half of our country. Likewise the chimney swift, known to everyone is the only representative of its family to live in this same region. Four other swifts and more than a dozen humming-birds visit the western U. S.

23c Not as in 23a or 23b. Figs. 402-404. ....**24**

24a Middle and outer toes joined for half their length, legs small. Bill straight, sharp pointed and longer than the head. Usually rather brilliantly colored. (Kingfishers).

Order CORACIIFORMES

Figure 402

Fig. 402. Belted Kingfisher, *Ceryte alcyon.* This bird is a familiar sight along many water courses. The nest is built in a horizontal hole cut 5 or 6 feet back into a creek bank. The birds' home is strewn with dead fish and other refuse and is not a model of good sanitation. Many species of Kingfishers are known to science.

24b Not as in 24a. Figs. 403 and 404. ....**25**

25a Toes always 3 in front and 1 behind, all on same level; hind toe as long as middle one, its claw usually longer than middle claw. Tail of twelve feathers. (The Perching Birds, or Song Birds.)

Order PASSERIFORMES

Figure 403

Fig. 403. Chipping Sparrow, *Spizella passerina*, (U. S. D. A.).
This largest order of birds includes many sizes, shapes and colors. The best singers are all included here.

25b Toes 2 in front, 2 behind, long compressed bill; tail feathers 10. (Cuckoos, Road Runners, etc.) **Order CUCULIFORMES**

Figure 404

Fig. 404. Yellow Billed Cuckoo, *Coccyzus americanus*, (U. S. D. A.). Besides telling the country side when it is "going to rain", this "Raincrow" eats quantities of woolly caterpillars which most birds refuse.

KEY TO THE MORE IMPORTANT ORDERS OF LIVING MAMMALS

1a Lay large eggs with leathery shells. (Duckbills and Spiny Ant- eaters.) **Order MONOTREMATA**

Figure 405

Fig. 405. a, Duckbill, *Ornithorhynchus anatinus*; b, Spiny Anteater, *Echidna aculeata*.
The young of these animals develop within their eggs much the same as birds but when they hatch they are fed on milk the same as any other mammal. Only Australia, Tasmania and New Guinea have animals of this order.

2a Pouched mammals. The young at birth very small and immature, completing their development in an outer "pocket" in abdomen of the mother. (Opossums, Kangaroos, Wombats, Treebears, Tasmanian Devil, etc.). **Order MARSUPIALIA**

Fig. 406. a, Common Opossum, *Didelphis virginiana*; b, Kangaroo, *Petrogale*.

The Opossum is the only marsupial in our region. Its well known habit of feigning death has immortalized it. Most of the marsupials are natives of Australia and the surrounding islands.

Figure 406

3d Fingers and toes ending in flattened nails instead of claws. First digit opposable to other digits. (Man, Lemurs, Monkeys and Apes.). **Order PRIMATES**

Fig. 407. a, Chimpanzee, *Pan troglodytes*; b, Man, *Homo sapiens*; c, Ruffed Lemur, *Lemur varius*.

The members of this order excell not in muscular strength so much as in intelligence. In this, Man greatly outstrips all the others; at least we say so.

Figure 407

4a Front limbs modified for flying. Bones of hand and fingers greatly elongated. (Bats). **Order CHIROPTERA**

Fig. 408. Red Bat, *Nycteris borealis*.

Several hundred species of bats are known. They are for the most part insect feeders though some feed on fruit. They do not get in ones hair or do the other evil things of which they are accused.

Figure 408

146

MAMMALS

4b Not as in 4a. Figs. 409-416. 5

5a Small furry mammals with sharp cusped teeth for eating insects. Mostly terrestrial. (Moles, Shrews and Hedgehogs).
                                    Order **INSECTIVORA**

Figure 409

Fig. 409. a, Hedgehog, *Erinaceus europaeus;* b, Common Mole, *Scalopus aquaticus;* c, Longtailed Shrew, *Sorex personatus.*

Hedgehogs and Porcupines are often confused. Their only similarity is in being covered with spines and in that they differ markedly. It will be noted that the Porcupine is a rodent and appears on the next page.

5b Not as in 5a. Figs. 410-416. 6

6a Flesh eating mammals (some vegetarian or omnivorous), with prominent canine teeth and small incisors. Molars fitted for cutting. 7

6b Not as in 6a. Figs. 412-416. 8

7a Large mammals with fin-like limbs; spend much of their time in water (Seals, Sealions and Walruses).   Order **PINNIPIDAE**

Figure 410

Fig. 410. a, Walrus, *Odobenus;* b, Alaska Fur Seal, *Callorhinus alascanus.*

A full-grown walrus is 10 to 12 feet long and weight around a ton. The tusks may measure two feet in length.

The Fur Seal was once threatened with extinction. It has figured prominently in international diplomacy. The animal has an outer coat of long stiff hairs which are removed to leave the silky soft fur used commercially.

147

MAMMALS

7b Feet normal and bearing claws (Dogs, Racoons, Bears, Cubs, etc.)
Order CARNIVORA

Figure 411

Fig. 411. a, Tiger, *Felis tigris*; b, Black Bear, *Ursa americanus*.
Bears are general favorites in the zoos and great outdoor preserves. If unspoiled by man they are good natured. They are among our rather few animals that walk on their entire foot (plantigrade). North America boasts almost 20 species of bears.

8a With prominent chisel shaped incisor teeth for gnawing. 9
8b With but small incisors or none. Figs. 414-416. 10
9a With two small peg-like incisors directly behind the larger ones at middle of upper jaw; tail small or seemingly absent. (Hares, Rabbits, Pikas). **Order LAGOMORPHA**

Figure 412

Fig. 412. a, Cottontail Rabbit, *Sylvilagus floridanus*; b, Pika or Cony, *Ochotona*.
Every one recognizes a rabbit at sight. The family has about 100 species in North America. The Pika or Little Chief Hare, as it is sometimes called, lives among the mountain rocks of our West. It is about the size of a small guinea pig and has no tail. It should not be confused with the old world Coneys which belong to a different order.

9b Upper jaw with but two incisors; tail usually long (Mice, Rats, Squirrels, Beavers, Gophers, Porcupines, etc.).
Order RODENTIA

Figure 413

Fig. 413. a, Canada Porcupine, *Erethizon dorsatus*; b, Gray Squirrel, *Sciurus carolinensis*; c, Grasshopper Mouse, *Onychomys leucogaster*.
The chipmunk is a lovable little fellow that furnishes the high lights for many a walk in the woods. Too little to be eaten by man it has been unmolested and is trustful. Flying squirrels are always interesting but do their sleeping by day and lose in popularity.
Mice and rats of which there are many species, are often highly destructive to field crops and stored foods.

148

10a No incisors; in some cases wholly toothless. (Sloths, Armadillos, Ant Bears.) Order EDENTATA

Fig. 414. a, Great Anteater, or Ant Bear, *Myrmecophaga jubata*; b, Two-toed Sloth, *Cholopus didactylus*; c, Armadillo, *Tatusia* sp.

The Armadillo has added much valuable information to our knowledge of identical quadruplets.

Figure 414

10b Body covered with large overlapping scales resembling a great pine cone. No teeth. (The Scaly Anteaters). Order PHILODOTA

Fig. 415. Pangolin, *Manis* sp.
These animals belong to Asia and Africa. There are several species. In food habits they are like the Edentates. Termites constitute much of their diet.

Figure 415

10c Strong burrowing mammals. (The Aard-Varks). Order TUBULIDENTATA

Fig. 416. Aard-Vark, *Orycteropus afer*.
This native of Africa burrows with the strongly clawed front legs. It does a valuable piece of service in keeping termites and locusts under control.

Figure 416

11a Nostrils extended into a long trunk or proboscis. Incisors forming tusks. (Elephants). Order PROBOSCIDEA

Fig. 417. a, African Elephant, *Loxodonta africanus*; b, Indian Elephant, *Elephas indicus*.
A large percentage of the elephants seen at the circus or in zoos are Indian elephants. Jumbo, P. T. Barnum's much advertised monster was an African elephant.

Figure 417

11b Without greatly elongated trunk. Figs. 418-421. 12

MAMMALS

12a Heavy marine forms with fore limbs flipper-like; hind limbs wanting; tail flattened horizontally. (Sea Cows, Manatees, etc.).

Order SIRENIA

Figure 418

Fig. 418. Manatee, *Trichechus*.
Found in Gulf of Mexico. They weigh up to 1500 pounds, and range up to 13 feet or more in length. They never come out on land. Florida protects them by heavy penalty.

12b Resembling the rodents in form; short tail, 3 toes in front, 4 behind all bearing hoofs. (Old World Coneys). Order HYRACOIDEA

Figure 419

Fig. 419. Old World Coney, *Procavia capensis*.
These small furry natives of Africa, Arabia and Syria are apparently most closely related to the rhinoceros. They are the Coneys referred to in the Scriptures.

13a Toes (2 or 4), even numbered. (Cow, Deer, Hog, Hippopotamus, Giraffe, Camel, etc.). Order ARTIODACTYLA

Figure 420

Fig. 420. a, Hippotamus; *Hippotamus amphibius*; b, Elk, *Cervus canadensis*; c, Giraffe, *Giraffe camelopardalis*; d, Domestic pig, *Sus*; e, One-Humped Camel, *Camelus dromedarius*.

13b Toes odd numbered (1, 3 or 5). (Horse, Rhinoceros, Tapir).

Order PERISSODACTYLA

Figure 421

Fig. 421. a, Common Zebra, *Equus zebra*; b, Tapir, *Tapirus terrestris*; c, Indian Rhinoceros, *Rhinoceros indicus*.
Rhinoceroses are near sighted, vindictive and dumb. Tapirs are found in both hemispheres. The one here pictured is a native of Brazil. Zebras come from Africa.

MAMMALS

14a With teeth. (Killer Whales, Dolphins, Porpoises, etc.).
Order ODONTOCETI

Figure 422

Fig. 422. a, Dolphin, *Delphinus delphus;* b, Killer Whale, *Orca orca.*
These animals very apparently once lived on land and later took up an aquatic life. Their teeth are cone shaped. The largest member of the order is the Sperm Whale which attains a length of 75 feet.

14b With plates of whale bone instead of teeth. (The Whalebone Whales).
Order MYSTACOCETI

Figure 423

Fig. 423. Sulphur-bottom Whale, *Balaenoptera musculus.*
This is the largest of all living animals. A large specimen will weigh close to 150 tons. Whale fishing is an old and profitable industry. Oil and whale bone are the principal returns but there are many by-products.

LET'S CALL IT A DAY

LIFE ZONES OF NORTH AMERICA

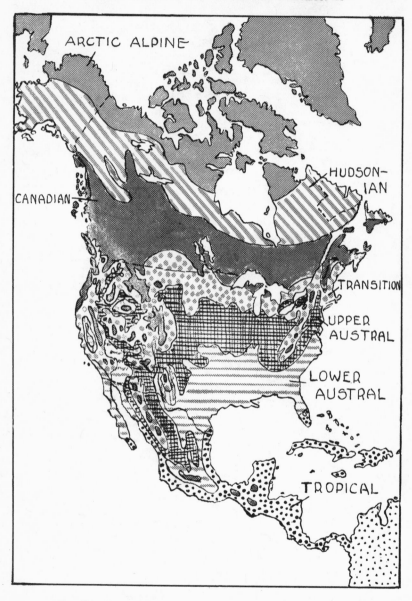

Fig. 424. For studying the distribution of plants and animals, the land areas of the earth have been divided into six regions. North America except its Tropical Zone, comprises the Nearctic Region The Zones of this region are shown on the map.

A PHYLOGENETIC LIST OF THE CLASSES AND ORDERS OF LIVING THINGS

CLASSIFICATION schemes are unstable affairs. Scientists attempt to arrange the plants and animals in their phylogenetic orders. By that we mean that they are grouped with references to their kinship. — the Smith's on one street; the Clark's on another. As biologists learn more about plants and animals their ideas of this relationship change. No two taxonomists would likely agree on the exact arrangement or terminology of a list as extensive as this. Our attempt has been to present a comprehensive list that represents modern scientific ideas but which is fairly close to the terminology found in the text books and manuals now in common use.

The list should be helpful in providing a view of the whole array of living things and to serve as a check list for collecting or museum purposes. The number in parenthesis which follows some of the group names, indicates the number of species of that group that are known to science. These numbers should be understood to be only approximate.

It will be noted that the phyla and orders have been given Arabic numbers, while the classes are numbered in Roman notation. If one uses P and A to designate the plant and the animal kingdom, respectively, then an index number may be readily given each order which will represent it as surely as its name, and at the same time show its proper position in relation to the other orders. These numbers are found useful in labeling museum and supply room materials and collections or data relating to Living Things. Materials arranged by these index numbers may be located at a moments notice. May we illustrate? One wishes to see specimens of "Glass Sponges" belonging to the order, Hexactinellida. Referring to this list the index number is found to be A 2-II-2. (A for animal kingdom; 2 for phylum Porifera; II for class Noncalcarae and the last 2 for the order Hexactinellida. If rooms, shelves and containers are marked with these characters and kept in their numerical order, any group, no matter how large the collection, may be located at will. Likewise Puffballs would be found at P 12-III-5; Roses, P 15-II-27; Oysters, A 15-IV-4 and Flying Fish A 16-IX-16.

PLANT KINGDOM

Division THALLOPHYTA

Sub-division Phycophyta (Algae)

Phylum 1 SCHIZOPHYTA
(Blue-green Algae)

Class I Myxophyceae
1. Chroococcales
2. Chamaesiphonales
3. Hormogonales

Phylum 2 EUGLENAPHYCEAE
1. Euglenales

Phylum 3 CHLOROPHYTA
(Green Algae)

Class I Chlorophyceae
1. Volvocales
2. Tetrasporales
3. Ulotrichales
4. Ulvales
5. Schizogoniales
6. Cladophorales
7. Oedogoniales
8. Zygnemotales
9. Chlorococcales
10. Siphonales
11. Siphonocladiales

Phylum 4 CHRYSOPHYTA

Class I Heterokontae
1. Heterochloridales
2. Rhizochloridales
3. Heterocapsales
4. Heterococcales
5. Heterotrichales
6. Heterosiphonales

Class II Chrysophyceae
1. Chrysomonadales
2. Rhizochrysidales
3. Chrysocapsales
4. Chrysotrichales

Class III Bacillarieae
(Diatoms) (5,000)
1. Centrales
2. Pennales

Phylum 5 PYRROPHYTA

Class I Dinophyceae
1. Gymnodiniales
2. Peridiniales
3. Dinophysidales
4. Rhizodiniales
5. Dinocapsales
6. Dinotrichales
7. Dinococcales

Phylum 6 PHAEOPHYTA
(Brown Algae) (1000)

Class I Isogeneratae
1. Ectocarpales
2. Sphacelariales
3. Tilopteridales
4. Cutleriales
5. Dictyotales

Class II Heterogeneratae
1. Chordariales
2. Sporochnales
3. Desmarestiales
4. Punctariales
5. Dictyosiponales
6. Laminariales (Kelps)

Class 3 Cyclosporeae
1. Fucales

Phylum 7 RHODOPHYTA
(Red Algae) (2500)

Class I Rhodophyceae
1. Bangiales
2. Nemalionales
3. Gelidiales
4. Cryptonemiales
5. Gigartinales
6. Rhodymeniales
7. Ceramiales

Phylum 8 CHAROPHYTA

Class I Charophyceae
1. Charales

Phylum 9 THE LICHENS (15,000)
(The components of these dual organisms belong to several groups of plants falling elsewhere but students of the phylum have assigned them to the following orders.)
1. Basidiolichenes
2. Ascolichenes

Sub-division Mycophyta (Fungi)
(56,000)

Phylum 10 SCHIZOMYCETES
(Bacteria)
1. Eubacteriales
2. Actinomycetales
3. Chlamydobachteriales
4. Thiobacteriales
5. Myxobacteriales
6. Spirochaetales
7. Caulobacteriales
8. Rickettsiales

Phylum 11 MYXOTHALLOPHYTA

Class I Myxomycetae
1. Endosporales
2. Exosporales

Class II Phytomyxinae
1. Plasmodiophorales

Class III Acrasiaeae
1. Acrasiales

Phylum 12 EUMYCETES
(True Fungi) (75,000)

Class I Phycomycetes
(Algal-like Fungi) (15,000)
1. Chytridales
2. Blastocladiales
3. Monoblepharidales
4. Ancylistales
5. Saprolegniales
6. Peronosporales
7. Mucorales
8. Entomophthorales

Class II Ascomycetes
(Sac Fungi) (25,00())
1. Saccharomycetales
2. Aspergilliales
3. Erysiphales
4. Hysteriales
5. Phacidiales
6. Pezizales
7. Tuberales
8. Helvellales
9. Exoascales
10. Hypocreales
11. Sphaeriales
12. Dothidiales
13. Laboulbeniales

Class III Basidiomycetes
(Club Fungi) (20,000)
1. Ustilaginales
2. Uredinales
3. Tremellales (Auriculariales)
4. Hymenomycetales
5. Gasteromycetales

Phylum 13 BRYOPHYTA (3,000)

Class I Musci (Mosses)
1. Sphagnales
2. Andreales
3. Bryales

Class II Hepaticae (Liverworts)
1. Jungermanniales
2. Metzgeriales
3. Marchantiales
4. Spaerocarpales
5. Anthocerotales

Phylum 14 PTERIDOPHYTA
(Ferns)
1. Filicales (4,000)
2. Equisetales (30)
3. Lycopodiales (500)

Phylum 15 SPERMATOPHYTA
(Seed-bearing Plants)

Class I Gymnospermae (500)
1. Cycadales
2. Ginkgoales
3. Coniferales
4. Gnetales

Class II Angiospermae (130,000)
Sub-class Monocotyledoneae
("Monocots")
1. Pandanales
2. Najadales
3. Graminales
4. Palmales
5. Cyclanthales
6. Arales
7. Xyridales
8. Liliales
9. Scitaminales
10. Orchidales

Sub-class Dicotyledoneae
("Dicots")
11. Casuarinales
12. Piperales
13. Juglandales
14. Myricales
15. Salicales
16. Fagales
17. Urticales
18. Santalales
19. Proteales
20. Aristolochiales
21. Polygonales
22. Chenopodiales
23. Caryophyllales
24. Ranunculales (Ranales)
25. Papaverales
26. Sarraceniales
27. Rosales
28. Geraniales
29. Sapindales
30. Rhamnales
31. Malvales
32. Violales
33. Begoniales
34. Opuntiales
35. Myrtales
36. Umbellales
37. Ericales
38. Primulales
39. Ebenales
40. Gentianales
41. Polemoniales
42. Plantaginales
43. Rubiales
44. Campanulales

ANIMAL KINGDOM

Phylum 1 PROTOZOA (15,000)

Class I Mastigophora
1. Chrysomonadida
(See Class Chrysophyceae in Plant Kingdom)
2. Cryptomonadida
(See Pyrophyta in Plant Kingdom)
3. Dinoflagellida
4. Phytomonadida
(See Order Volvocales in Plant Kingdom)
5. Euglenida
6. Pantostomatida
7. Protomonadida
8. Polymastigida
9. Hypermastigida

Class II Sarcodina
1. Proteomyxa
2. Mycetozoa
(See Myxothallophyta in Plant Kingdom)
3. Amoebaea
4. Testacea
5. Foraminifera
6. Heliozoa
7. Radiolaria

Class III Sporozoa
1. Gregarinida
2. Coccidia
3. Haemosporidia
4. Myxosporidia
5. Actinomyxidia

6. Microsporidia
7. Sarcosporidia
8. Haplosporidia

Class IV Ciliata
1. Opalinida
2. Holotrichida
3. Heterotrichida
4. Oligotrichida
5. Hypotrichida
6. Peritrichida

Class V Suctoria

Phylum 2 PORIFERA
(Sponges) (3,000)

Class I Calcarea
1. Homocoela
2. Heterocoela

Class II Noncalcarea
1. Myxospongeda
2. Hexactinellida
3. Tetraxonida
4. Keratosa

Phylum 3 COELENTERATA
(9,500)

Class I Hydrozoa
1. Hydrariae
2. Hydrocorallinae
3. Tubulariae
4. Campanulariae
5. Trachomedusae
6. Narcomedusae
7. Siphonophora

Class II Scyphozoa
1. Stauromedusae
2. Coronatae
3. Cubomedusae
4. Semaeostomae
5. Rhizostomae

Class III Anthozoa
1. Alcyonaria
2. Zoantharia

Phylum 4 CTENOPHORA
(Comb Jellies) (100)

Class I Tentaculata
1. Cydippida
2. Lobata
3. Cestida

Class II Nuda
1. Beroidea

Phylum 5 PLATYHELMINTHES
(Flat Worms) (6,500)

Class I Turbellaria
1. Acoela
2. Rhabdocoelida
3. Tricladida
4. Polycladida
5. Temnocephalida

Class II Trematoda
Sub-class *Monogenea*
1. Monopisthodiscea
2. Monopisthocotylea
3. Polyopisthocotylea
Sub-class *Digenea*
4. Gasterostomata
5. Prosostomata

Class III Cestoidea
Sub-class *Cestodaria*
1. Amphilinidea
2. Gryocotylidea
Sub-class *Cestodes*
3. Tetrophyllidea
4. Pseudophyllidea
5. Tetrarhynchidea
6. Cyclophyllidea

Class IV Nemertinea (Nemertea)
1. Protonemertina
2. Mesonemertina
3. Metanemertina
4. Heteronemertina

Phylum 6 NEMATHELMINTHES
(Round Wosms) (3,500)

Class I Nematoda
1. Hologonia
2. Telogonia

Class II Nematomorpha
1. Gordioidea
2. Nectonematoidea

Class III Acanthocephala
1. Echinorhynchoidea

Phylum 7 ROTIFERA
(Trochelminthes) (1,500)

Class I Rotatoria
1. Seisonidea
2. Bdelloidea
3. Monogononta

Class II Gastrotricha
1. Macrodasyoidea
2. Chaetonotoidea

Class III Kinorhyncha
1. Echinodera

Phylum 8 BRYOZOA
(Moss-like Animals) (2,000)

Class I Entoprocta

Class II Ectoprocta
1. Phylactolaemata
2. Cyclostomata
3. Chilostomata
4. Ctenostomata

Phylum 9 BRACHIOPODA
(125)
1. Ecardines
2. Testicardines

Phylum 10 PHORONIDEA
(15)

Phylum 11 CHAETOGNATHA
(30)

Phylum 12 ECHINODERMATA
(5,000)

Class I Asteroidea
1. Phanerozonia
2. Spinulosa
3. Forcipulata

Class II Ophiuroidea
1. Ophiurae
2. Euryalae

Class III Echinoidea
1. Endocyclica
2. Clypaestroida
3. Spatangoida

Class IV Holothurioidea
1. Aspidochirota
2. Dendrochirota
3. Molpadonia
4. Apoda

Class V Crinoidea
1. Neo-crinoidea

Phylum 13 MOLLUSCA
(80,000)

Class I Amphineura
1. Polyplacophora
2. Aplacophora

Class II Gastropoda
1. Prosobranchiata
2. Opistobranchiata
3. Pulmonata

Class III Scaphopoda

Class IV Pelecypoda
1. Protobranchiata
2. Filibranchiata
3. Eulamellibranchiata
4. Pseudolamellibranchiata

Class V Cephalopoda
1. Tetrabranchiata
2. Debranchiata

Phylum 14 ANNELIDA
(5,000)

Class I Archiannelida

Class II Polychaeta
1. Polychaeta errantia
2. Polychaeta sedentaria

Class III Oligochaeta

Class IV Gephyrea
1. Echiurida
2. Sipunculida
3. Priapulida

Class V Hirudinea
(Leeches)
1. Rhynchobdellida
2. Gnathobdellida

Phylum 15 ARTHROPODA
(713,625)

Class I Crustacea (24,750)
Sub-class Entomastraca
1. Branchiopoda
2. Copepoda
3. Ostracoda
4. Cirripedia
Sub-class Malacostraca
5. Leptostraca
6. Mysidacea
7. Cumacea
8. Amphipoda
9. Isopoda
10. Stomatopoda
11. Euphausiacea
12. Decapoda

Class II Onychophora (75)

Class III Myriapoda (2,800)
1. Pauropoda
2. Diplopoda
3. Chilopoda
4. Symphyla

Class IV Insecta (640,000)
1. Thysanura
2. Collembola
3. Plecoptera
4. Ephemerida
5. Odonata
6. Embiidina
7. Orthoptera
8. Zoraptera
9. Isoptera
10. Dermaptera
11. Coleoptera
12. Strepsiptera
13. Thysanoptera
14. Corrodentia
15. Mallophaga
16. Anoplura
17. Hemiptera
18. Homoptera
19. Neuroptera
20. Trichoptera
21. Lepidoptera
22. Mecoptera
23. Diptera
24. Siphonaptera
25. Hymenoptera

Class V Arachnida (46,000)
1. Scorpionida (600)
2. Pedipalpi
3. Araneida (15,000)
4. Palpigrada
5. Pseudoscorpionida
6. Solpugida
7. Phalangida (2,000)
8. Acarina (8,000)
9. Xiphosura
10. Linguatulida
11. Pycnoganida
12. Tardigrada

Phylum 16 CHORDATA (40,000)

Subphylum Enteropneusta
1. Balanoglossida

Subphylum Tunicata

Class II Larvacea

Class III Ascidiacea
1. Krikobranchia
2. Dictyobranchia
3. Ptychbranchia
4. Pyrosomida

Class IV Thaliacea
1. Multistigmatea
2. Astigmatea

Subphylum Cephalochorda
1. Cirrostomi

Subphylum Vertebrata (Craniata)

Class VI Cyclostomata
1. Myxinoidea
2. Petromyzontia

Class VII Elasmobranchii
1. Euselachii (Sharks)
2. Cyclospondyli (Basking Sharks)
3. Batoidei (Rays)

Class VIII Holocephali
1. Chimaeroidei

Class IX Pisces (Fish) (15,000)

Super Order Ganoidei
1. Selachostomi
2. Glaniostomi
3. Ginglymodi
4. Halecomorphi
5. Dipnoi

Super Order Teleostei
6. Isospondyli
7. Enchelycephali
8. Colocephali
9. Eventognathi
10. Nematognathi
11. Iniomi
12. Haplomi (Pike)
13. Cyprinodontes
14. Salmopercae
15. Xenarchi

16. Synentognathi
17. Lophobranchi
18. Hemibranchii
19. Anacanthini
20. Selenichthyes
21. Heterosomata
22. Acanthopteri
23. Pharyngognathi
24. Cataphracti
25. Discocephali
26. Gobioides
27. Haplodoci
28. Xenopterygii
29. Deripia
30. Plectognathi
31. Pediculati

Class X Amphibia (1,750)
1. Apoda
2. Caudata (Urodela)
3. Salientia (Anura)

Class XI Reptila (4,000)
1. Testudinata
2. Rhynchocepalia
3. Crocodilia
4. Lacertilia
5. Serpentes

Class XII Aves (Birds) (12,000)
1. Struthioniformes
2. Rheiformes
3. Casuariiformes
4. Tinamiformes
5. Apterygiformes
6. Sphenisciformes
7. Gaviiformes
8. Colymbiformes
9. Procellariiformes
10. Pelicaniformes
11. Ciconiiformes
12. Anseriformes
13. Falconiformes
14. Galliformes
15. Gruiformes
16. Charadriiformes
17. Columbiformes
18. Psittaciformes
19. Cuculiformes
20. Strigiformes
21. Caprimulgiformes
22. Micropodiformes
23. Trogoniformes
24. Coraciiformes
25. Piciformes
26. Passeriformes

Class XIII Mammalia
(Hairy Animals) (4,000)
Sub-class I Prototheria
1. Monotremata

Sub-cass II Metatheria
2. Marsupialia

Sub-class III Eutheria
3. Insectivora
4. Dermoptera
5. Chiroptera
6. Carnivora
7. Pinnipidae
8. Primates
9. Edentata
10. Pholidota
11. Tubulidentata
12. Rodentia
13. Lagomorpha
14. Perissodactyla
15. Artiodactyla
16. Hyracoidea
17. Proboscidea
18. Sirenia
19. Odontoceti
20. Mystacoceti

INDEX AND PICTURED GLOSSARY

INDEX

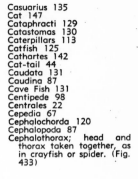

Figure 434

Figure 435

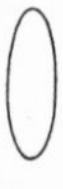

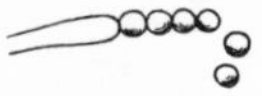

D

Figure 436

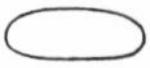

INDEX

Figure 439

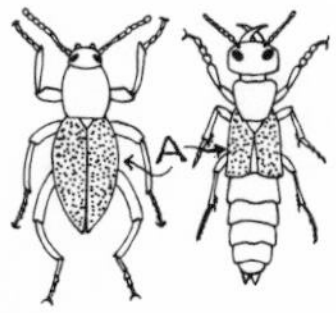

Figure 437

Figure 438

Figure 440

Figure 441

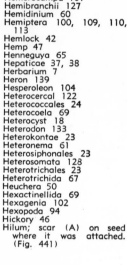

Figure 442

INDEX

INDEX

Figure 445

Figure 446

Figure 447

Figure 448

INDEX

Figure 449

Figure 450

Figure 451

INDEX

Figure 452

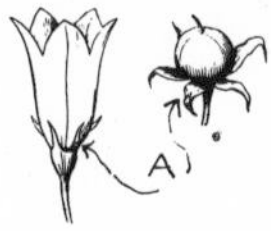

Figure 453

Figure 454

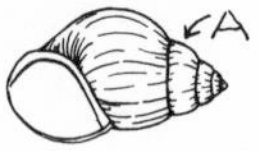